BIRDS OF AUSTRALIA

BIRDS OF AUSTRALIA

Colin Harrison

Bison Books

First published in 1988 by
Bison Books Ltd
176 Old Brompton Road
London SW5 0BA
England

ISBN 0-86124-418-4

Printed in Hong Kong

Page 1: *The Rainbow Lorikeet* Trichoglossus haematodus *is one of Australia's most widespread parrots, and one of its most colourful.*

Pages 2-3: *The Laughing Kookaburra* Dacelo gigas *is a species of kingfisher although it lives in woodland and feeds mainly on insects and small reptiles.*

Pages 4-5: *Fogg Dam Sanctuary in the Northern Territory. In this part of Australia there is an annual wet season when these tropical swamplands offer ideal habitat for wetland birds.*

Contents

Australia has a rich, varied, and in some respects, unique birdlife. In addition to those species that are resident, it gains others because it is at the end of the winter migration routes from northern-hemisphere landmasses, and because it is far enough south to be reached occasionally by many of the seabirds exploiting the rich antarctic seas. Its total possible avifauna currently exceeds 725 species, with other accidental strays likely to be added to the list later. About 530 of these are landbirds.

It is impossible to encompass all of them in a book of this size and scope. What I have tried to do is to ensure that as much as possible that is of special interest gains a mention, and to build up a picture of the variety of birds present. Because the presence of different birds is so closely related to the landscape in which they live, I have taken the main zones of differing vegetation and environment and indicated the type of birds occurring in each, and the way in which they relate to their surroundings.

However briefly, it has been possible to mention about half the landbirds, but rather fewer of those occurring on waters or the surrounding coasts and seas. Choosing one species and omitting another have been very difficult tasks, but I hope that the resulting text presents a useful and enjoyable overview of Australian birds.

1
A Special Birdlife:
The Legacy of the Past

Birds occur almost everywhere so we tend to take them for granted. They are a part of the landscape from bush to city and from desert to sea; and we are so accustomed to them that we overlook their inherent oddity.

Birds resemble reptiles although this feature is perhaps best seen in the naked nestlings, or in a bird undergoing heavy moult. They differ from reptiles in that they are able to control their body temperature without relying on the conditions surrounding them. This has enabled them to invade almost every part of the world. Birds also have a body covering of feathers, probably evolved from modified scales, which form a continuous overlapping cover which can be sleeked down or fluffed up to help with temperature control.

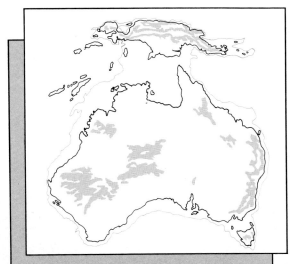

The fringe of larger feathers attached to the forelimbs and to the shortened relic of a tail that once formed the feathered wings and tail probably developed later; but as soon as birds had them, and used them for flight, their whole way of life was changed. The big, overlapping fans of feathers that could be folded away when not in use were wonderful structures, but the need to move and rest in ways which did not damage them and to avoid wearing them out through too much contact with trees, plants or the ground, imposed limitations. In return for gaining freedom of movement in the air, birds became constrained in other ways.

For example, weight hindered flight and the body structure became modified to be as light as possible, with thin, hollow bones. Food had to be of a concentrated kind and not too bulky; and because eggs and young could not be carried, nesting became a necessity.

Flight is more than a straightforward flapping movement and, during the period that our present families of flying birds have existed, wings and tails have become increasingly specialized for different kinds of flight in ways that we can easily recognize. The short, rather rounded wings, typical of many small birds, are good general-purpose wings mainly for short flights among vegetation. Tails function as brakes and rudders, and the long tails, which many small, skulking birds seem to have, help them to weave rapidly among the tangles of stems and branches in which they live. Some larger birds have fairly broad, rounded wings on which the main primary feathers taper; and, on a spread wing, the tips splay out like fingers on a hand. This type of wing enables the bird to manoeuvre quickly. Birds, such as the Collared Sparrowhawk *Accipiter cirrocephalus*, where such wings are combined with a longish tail, demonstrate this well. The tail helps the bird to twist and dodge rapidly

Left: *The Yellow-spotted Honeyeater* Meliphaga notata *is a typical member of this big Australian family of nectar- and insect-eating birds. It shows the head pattern which characterizes the species.*

through woodland and scrub in pursuit of small birds on which it preys.

Narrower and more tapering wings occur on other species and allow a faster flight in more open places or high in the air; these birds often combine rapid flight with gliding to economize in effort and use of energy. Examples can be seen in the woodswallows which hawk for flying insects. Better examples perhaps are the Welcome and White-backed Swallows, *Hirundo neoxena* and *Cheramoeca leucosterna* which combine finely tapering wings with well-forked tails that enable the birds to twist, turn, make rapid circles, or even check their flight in mid-air. The Fork-tailed Swift *Apus pacificus*, a blackish bird with white on its rump and throat, has long, slender, tapering wings and a deeply forked tail. In the northern hemisphere, it nests in eastern Eurasia and comes to Australia as a non-breeding visitor. It flies rapidly, circling and gliding with occasional wingbeats, catching insects in the air in its wide-gaped mouth, and drinking by swooping low over water and snatching up a mouthful. At night, it climbs to greater heights and sleeps circling on the wing. It is possible that it never settles except when it nests and that non-breeding birds just keep flying. Its greatest threat is from heavy rain and it may travel considerable distances to fly around storms and areas of bad weather.

Long, tapering wings provide fast flight over long distances. This can be seen in some of the nomadic parrots, and also in the many wading shorebirds that visit Australia from the distant arctic tundra to escape the northern hemisphere winter. Wings of this type are also used to great effect by birds of prey, particularly falcons, such as the Little Falcon *Falco longipennis*. This raptor flies down birds in the open, and provides an interesting contrast in adaptation to the Sparrowhawk mentioned earlier.

There are some odd parallels to the swift among a family of long-winged, fork-tailed, and mainly aerial seabirds with small, little-used feet – the frigatebirds – but, in comparison to the swifts, these birds are giants and must snatch their food from the surface of the sea or harry other seabirds, forcing them to disgorge their food.

Wings are not only used for fast movement, however. Skilful use of rising air currents may enable a bird to stay aloft and to travel for long distances with little effort and minimum expenditure of energy. This is very important for larger birds for which it may be a long time and distance between meals. Flying over the land, such birds make use of thermals, the currents of warm air rising from ground heated by the sun. This requires a subtle use of varying, unpredictable currents and, like the birds that dodge among trees, the big land gliders tend to have broad wings with splay-'fingered' tips. A broad, spreading tail usually accom-

panies these. An example of this is the Wedge-tailed Eagle *Aquila audax* that will soar for hours over open country watching for moving prey or for the carcass of a recently dead animal.

In contrast, birds that spend most of their time over the sea have fewer problems with turbulent air, but they do need the greatest spread possible to make use of the small updraughts of air that rise where the wind strikes the ridges formed by waves. Very long, narrow, tapering wings have evolved. These are seen at their best in the shearwaters, and especially the albatrosses, which may travel for long periods with hardly a wingflap, using long, level gliding or an undulating flight relying on the lift given by the air currents from large waves.

Tails are of little importance here. Such flight can carry birds for enormous distances but these long, narrow wings do not allow for quick manoeuvring. Both landing and takeoff can be difficult, requiring sloping sites, raised jumping-off points, or long runs with few obstructions. This limits the type of land they can use for breeding.

Some birds seem to manage without flying and, in regions where ground predators are scarce or absent, they may have lost the ability to fly altogether. New Zealand is the most outstanding example of an isolated country where this has occurred; but, in Australia, the Plains Wanderer *Pediono-*

Above: Here seen bathing, the broad-winged Collared Sparrowhawk Accipiter cirrhocephalus *relies on surprise to catch its prey.*
Right: Longer, more slender wings which taper in flight; large, deep-set eyes; and a broad-based bill mark this Masked Wood Swallow Artamus personatus *as an aerial insect hunter.*

mus torquatus and the scrub-birds and bristlebirds seem to be moving in that direction, and have powers of flight that are very weak and little used.

Birds' legs and feet seem less strikingly adapted than wings, but they are equally varied. The typical bird foot has three toes directed forwards and one backwards. This is a pattern that seems more useful for perching than for walking and, in fact, most birds which habitually perch, move on the ground by hopping. The widespread occurrence of the typical bird foot suggests that the walking adaptation came later in evolutionary terms than the perching adaptation.

Birds that spend a lot of time on the ground usually have relatively long legs; for example, the Willie Wagtail *Rhipidura leucophrys* and the Giant Cuckoo-shrike *Coracina maxima*. To enable ground-living birds to run, the toes are reduced in length. This is apparent in stone curlews, the Bustard *Eupodotis australis*, and the Emu *Dromaius novaehollandiae*. Conversely, birds that paddle on soft surfaces have longer toes. This can be seen to some extent among the

shorebirds and herons that must move on mud, more so in the swamp-living rails, and at its most extreme in the Lotusbird *Irediparra gallinacea*. About half of this small wader appears to consist of long legs and feet with long toes carrying long, straight claws. These spread the load and allow it to walk across the floating vegetation and lilypads of the ponds and lagoons on which it lives.

Birds that swim need to have broad-surfaced toes to provide propulsion. This is mainly achieved in grebes and the Coot *Fulica atra* by flattened lobes on the toes. The partly aquatic Red-necked Avocet *Recurvirostra novaehollandiae* and the Magpie-goose *Anseranas semipalmatus* both have partly webbed toes, but toes are fully webbed in other waterfowl and in the seabirds. In the various families of birds related to the pelicans and cormorants, the Pelicaniformes, the webbing extends to all four of the toes.

In birds, such as kingfishers and cuckoos, that squat on branches for long periods to watch and wait, two toes are directed forwards and two backwards. Parrots and the Osprey *Pandion haliaetus* can reverse the outer toe as an aid when feeding and, in the parrots, the legs are short and muscular and the foot can be rotated to help the birds to climb. Parrots can also use their strong bills as a kind of third 'leg' when climbing.

Once the forelimbs of birds had been modified to form wings, they had to rely wholly on their bills to be able to feed successfully. Early on in evolution, teeth were replaced by the sharp-edged, elongated jaws that could pick up precisely and manipulate small objects. It was difficult to break up food, and most was swallowed whole. Digestion was relied upon to break down the food internally. Seed-eating birds have a muscular gizzard containing grit which is replaced periodically, and muscular action is used to grind the seeds into digestible form.

Not until later did some birds evolve such that the foot could be used to hold food while it is being broken up. Birds of

Below: *The long, slender wings and deeply forked tail of the Welcome Swallow* Hirundo neoxena *indicate its agility in pursuing flying insects.*

Above: *Almost all wings and tail, the Fork-tailed Swift* Apus pacificus *spends most of its life on the wing.*

prey, swamphens, parrots, and some insect-eating songbirds have this ability; but it is lacking in the butcherbirds which could have made good use of it.

Insect-eaters, which pick up small prey, tend to have thin, pointed bills. Those that rely on catching them in mid-air need a wider 'net'. Flycatchers tend to have extra-wide bills for this purpose. The most extreme is that of the Boat-billed Flycatcher *Machaerirhynchus flaviventris*. Seen in side view, its bill is rather long and slightly stout, but seen from above it is almost as wide as the head itself. In spite of this, its flycatching performance does not seem exceptional. Swallows and swifts seem to have small bills but, when these open fully, the gape seems almost to split the head in half. Nightjars have even larger gapes and, as in some of the flycatchers, they are bordered on either side by long bristles that help to make them a more effective 'trawl' for flying insects.

Birds that probe after small creatures have long, slender bills. In the various species of mud- and sand-probing shorebirds they show all degrees of elongation. Proportionally, snipe have the longest bills of all. In this bird, the bill is so long that, at times, it looks awkward to manage. It is plunged deep into soft mud. The end of it is flexible and equipped with sensitive nerve endings. These enable the bird to detect, seize, and eat worms and similar prey with the bill submerged. These birds do not have to be able to see to feed so that they do so mainly at night when they are less vulnerable to predators. The slender bill of the Avocet is peculiarly upcurved, as is that of the visiting Terek Sandpiper *Tringa terek*; and this type of bill is swung from side to side in muddy water to find and seize small prey. The converse are the long, down-curved bills of the Whimbrel *Numenius phaeopus* and Eastern Curlew *N. madagascariensis*. These are designed for probing for, and withdrawing, the tunnelling worms of estuarine and coastal mudflats.

For birds that need to grasp large, slippery fish or squid,

Above: *A fast-flying, narrow-winged raptor, the Little Falcon* Falco longipennis *uses old nests of crows or hawks.*

Below: *Soaring birds, such as eagles and this Brahminy Kite* Haliastur indus, *have broad wings with feather tips splayed to use the rising currents of warm air.*

the bill is often equipped with a sharp hook at the tip. This can be seen in albatrosses, shearwaters, cormorants, pelicans, and other such species. The cormorants have an expandable skin pouch in the throat that will accommodate temporarily a very large fish. In the Pelican *Pelicanus conspicillatus* this has been modified into a large, long pouch the length of the lower bill. This expands while the flexible bones of the lower mandible arch outwards as the bird snatches at a shoal of fish, and then, as the head is raised, it can be contracted to squeeze out the water and retain the fish.

A dabbling duck has a flattened, water-sifting bill which, with the help of the tongue, pumps water through a grill of fine ridges just inside the bill, extracting tiny food particles. This is highly developed in the big-billed Shoveler *Anas rhynchotis*, and even more in the highly specialized Pink-eared Duck *Malacorhynchus membranaceus* in which the great bill, that gives it a front-heavy look, is extended at either side of the tip by flexible, fleshy flanges to cover a greater area.

Birds which eat hard food, such as seeds, have short, stout bills. The House Sparrow *Passer domesticus* and grass-finches have seed-cracking bills which are also beautifully adapted to manipulate and rotate a small seed with a little help from the tongue. The bird shears away the husk, which falls to the ground, while the kernel is swallowed.

Parrots' bills are crushers and strippers, used to demolish twigs, branches, woody cones, fruits, and also hard seeds. They appear to be designed for woodland destruction, but these stout bills which can, in the case of the Black Cockatoo *Calyptorhynchus funereus*, shred the iron-hard wood of Jarrah trees, can also manipulate small seeds. The tip of the lower mandible works against the inside of the curved upper mandible and, as seeds are split and husked, the tongue helps to extract the edible kernel. These bills are outstandingly finely evolved feeding tools. There is at least one kind of songbird which has a tearing bill. The Crested Shrike-tit *Falcunculus frontatus* seems to be a kind of whistler that has evolved a stout parrot-type bill for tearing and levering at the bark of gum trees to get at hidden insects.

The nectar from flowers can be an important food for birds, and many Australian birds, such as the large family of honeyeaters, are adapted to feed on it. Having a slender bill that can be inserted deeply into flowers is not enough. In these species, the tip of the tongue is finely split into filaments to form a brush-tip that can take up larger amounts of nectar. The flowers also gain because birds transfer pollen from one plant to another, ensuring successful fertilization and seeding. Some tubular-shaped flowers are specifically adapted to be fertilized by birds. The lorikeets, in the parrot family, also feed on nectar but, with their short, stubby bills, they rely on the short, open, and multistamened flowers of eucalypts and similar plants. They, too, have brush tongues to help them feed. Because these birds do not eat insects, how do they provide their young with enough body-building proteins?

The answer seems to be that they take pollen as well as nectar.

There is another important function for which birds' bills have evolved – building the great variety of nests which can be found. Because flying birds must be lightweight, a female only produces one egg in her body at a time. Then she lays it with others in a specially constructed nest and uses the warmth of her body to incubate the clutch. Only the megapodes, mentioned in later chapters, have taken advantage of exceptional conditions and managed to dispense with incubation.

We can see how the varied structural adaptations of birds would allow them to exploit the various habitats of the environment in which they live. In spite of their potential mobility, however, birds do not move around and colonize new places as freely as might be expected. Indeed, it has been suggested that birds evolved the power of flight to stay in the same place! This idea seems more reasonable if we consider the birds that live on small, windswept islands. Birds are constrained by limits of geographical distribution; some of which only make sense if we look at the geological and climatic history of Australia, and realize how that has affected the land's birdlife.

Australia is a great continental landmass which, in the distant past, was part of an even greater one known as Gondwanaland, centred in the southern hemisphere. About 100 million years ago, this supercontinent began to fragment, and whole continents – South America, Africa, the Indian peninsula, Australia, and New Zealand – separated and began to move northwards, leaving Antarctica behind.

We can visualize Australia as a great 'plate' of land, at times partly submerged, gradually sliding northwards in the Pacific region; and, as it encountered resistance beneath the sea from the area towards which it was moving, it forced upwards at that edge ridges of land which became New Guinea. Not only was the connection between Australia and New Guinea submerged under seawater but, for much of this earlier period as a separate continent, the low centre of Australia, in the region of Lake Eyre and northwards, was a sea. In early times, it was sometimes connected with the

Left: *A Black-browed Albatross* Diomedea melanophrys. *hanging in an updraught, shows the streamlined body and the very long, narrow wings used in its prolonged gliding flight.*

Above: *Although it is a ground feeder with long legs for walking, the Giant Cuckoo-shrike* Coracina maxima *builds a neat, shallow, tree nest like its arboreal relatives.*
Below: *The Lotusbird* Irediparra gallinacea *runs on lily pads with its long-toed feet and builds its sketchy nest there, too.*

Above: *Wading deeply on its long legs in saline or brackish water, the Red-necked Avocet* Recurvirostra novaehollandiae *seeks food with sideways sweeps of the submerged, upcurved bill.*

Below: *The seemingly narrow bill of the Boat-billed Flycatcher* Machaerirhynchus flaviventris *is as broad as its head.*

oceans at its southern end via the Great Australian Bight and in the north at the Gulf of Carpentaria. It then divided the land into two islands, but later, as land levels changed, it became an inland sea.

When the Gondwanaland break-up began, birds were already evolving the major differences which we now recognize between the different orders and families. The area of Australia, New Guinea, and some adjacent islands was already receiving an avifauna, some of which would remain unique to it, or later spread from it. The emus and cassowaries probably date from this period; and this would seem to have been the centre of origin for the 'moundbuilders' or megapodes, the big-footed birds that bury their eggs in warm places instead of incubating them.

Many other Australian birds are representatives of widespread, sometimes world-ranging families, and it is difficult to know when they first arrived. What is certain is that Australia and New Guinea were isolated from other large landmasses in such a way that they did not receive the big influxes of evolving species that had originated elsewhere and were shared by other continents. Some birds, which may have originated elsewhere, found conditions to their liking when they arrived in Australia. If the birds with which they had competed for living space elsewhere were not present here, they could diversify and new species could evolve to fill the vacant ecological niches. Parrots provide an example of this. They proliferated to produce the present array of brightly coloured species ranging in habitat from forest to spinifex grassland, marshes and sea coasts.

The pigeons were another successful group, and they produced, among others, some inland terrestrial forms that take the place of the gamebirds found on other continents. They share these gamebird niches with a variety of buttonquails. The latter are another group which may have been derived from a successful early invasion of Australia, or they might have originated on the continent. One other group which has produced a number of successful forms ranging from the large to the tiny, and from swamps to dry interior, is the kingfishers.

The most notable success story is that of the Australian songbirds, the so-called passerine family. A small number of those now present in the Australian birdlife are representatives of families found elsewhere. They usually have only one or two species and, in evolutionary terms, are probably invaders of relatively recent origin. In addition, there are many groups of species which appear similar to songbirds elsewhere, mostly those of the oriental region, Asia and Africa. They tend to show slight peculiarities and do not wholly resemble the others; but the simplest explanation accepted in the past was to assume that the ancestral forms were representatives of these outside groups which had invaded Australia from the north and had developed their differences later, and in isolation. In the last few years, however, studies of the genetic material, the DNA chains, in the body cells of these birds, appear to reveal a different story.

It would seem that, at some very early period, Australia, a continent lacking such small songbirds and with a potential for being colonized, was invaded by an ancestral stock of birds related to the crows. These songbirds spread to occupy the vacant ecological niches, adapted to their new conditions, and many new species evolved.

Those who study birds, or indeed any group of complex organisms, constantly encounter a phenomenon known as 'convergence'. Expressed simply, it means that if two species of quite different origin and appearance begin to live in the same type of habitat, pursuing the same way of life, taking the same type of food in the same way, adapting to similar environmental conditions, then they will evolve to a point where they may show an extraordinarily close resemblance. This happened in the case of Australian songbirds. They produced forms resembling the flycatchers, thrushes, warblers, babblers, tits, magpies, chats, and nuthatches that occurred

The Painted Snipe Rostratula benghalensis, *not a true snipe, shows the typical slender, probing, shorebird bill. The patterned plumage is for camouflage when resting in grasses.*

elsewhere in the Old World. This caused the confusion which baffled many people studying Australian birds in the nineteenth century. From what we now know, it would appear that Australia has its own, unique, avifauna, adapted to its range of habitats and more closely related to one another than to apparently similar species elsewhere.

The list of these endemic birds of the Australian and New Guinea region is impressive. It includes lyrebirds, scrubbirds, bowerbirds, Australian treecreepers, blue wrens, emu-wrens, grasswrens, honeyeaters, chats, thornbills, scrubwrens, whitefaces, bristlebirds, pardalotes, Australo-Papuan robins and flycatchers, Chowchillas, Australo-Papuan babblers, quail-thrushes, whipbirds, Australian choughs, drongos, magpie-larks, fantails, birds-of-paradise, woodswallows, currawongs, orioles, and cuckoo-shrikes.

In addition to receiving immigrant species, Australia appears also to have contributed significantly to faunas elsewhere. Species such as drongos, fantails, cuckoo-shrikes, and woodswallows have settled in the oriental region as far north as India; monarch flycatchers are into Africa; and there is an oriole in Europe.

Besides convergence, there is another evolutionary trend that creates problems in understanding relationships. It can be seen in the group of seed-eaters which, finding no competitors, settled in Australia and evolved new forms. These were the grassfinches. They belong to the waxbill family in which a major group, the mannikins, extends from the oriental region into Africa and Australia. Its species are mostly coloured in shades of brown and black. In Africa and in Australia, there are two other groups, mostly more brightly coloured: the waxbills in Africa; the grassfinches in Australia. As these basically related groups have evolved to occupy different habitats, some surprisingly similar forms have been produced.

The green-and-grey Red-browed Finch *Aegintha temporalis* of eastern Australia is so superficially similar to some of

the typical African waxbills of the genus *Estrilda* that it was once thought to be one of them.The Crimson Finch *Neochmia phaeton* of northern Australia resembles, in its slaty crown, scarlet face and underside, and black belly, some African firefinches of the genus *Lagonosticta*, mimicking them even down to the vestigial white spots at the sides of the breast. There are other, less exact analogies, such as between the Beautiful Firetail *Emblema bella* of south-eastern Australia and the Blackeared Waxbill *Estrilda erythronotos* of Africa. This type of similarity evolved by related birds in different geographical regions is sometimes known as 'parallelism'.

Over a long period of prehistory these and other groups of birds helped to create Australia's specialized avifauna. The birdlife that had built up over tens of millions of years, however, was to be affected dramatically in the last few million years by widespread climatic changes. Australia's gradual northward shift had brought it into the present-day desert zones of the earth, and it occupies much the same position in the southern hemisphere as does the Sahara Desert of North Africa in the northern hemisphere. Increasing aridity tended to reduce its inland lakes and the apparently widespread forests.

Even more significant, however, have been the climatic fluctuations of the last 2 million years. This period spans the latter part of the geological period known as the Pliocene, and the last 1700000 years encompasses the Pleistocene period. The whole of this span was affected by a rhythmic series of long-term climatic fluctuations, from warm to cold and back again. The fluctuations became more marked in the Pleistocene period, and the colder periods were so cold that ice not only increased and spread at the poles, but great icecaps were formed on some of the other continents, only to melt again during the next warm period. Because of these changes, the Pleistocene is often known as the Ice Age.

For a long time it was thought that only four to six major

Largest of the waterside shorebirds, the Eastern Curlew Numenius madagascariensis *combines the long legs of a wader with the long, decurved bill that probes deeply into mud and worm burrows.*

climatic fluctuations had occurred during the Pleistocene, but we now know that there were some seventeen periods of about 90000 to 100000 years, and that during each of these there was a cold period and a warm period. The Ice Ages are said to have ended about 10000 years ago at the end of the last cold period, but many geologists believe that the period in which we live is just a warm interglacial period of a continuing series of ice ages.

Near the poles these changes produced alternations of temperate and polar conditions. Whole zones of plants and animals shifted away from the poles and back again as climates changed. A movement of forest or grassland may be difficult to envisage but, if we remember that these changes took place over thousands or tens of thousands of years, it is possible to see how one type of vegetation could slowly replace another and take with it the animals typically associated with it.

Problems would arise where populations of living things became isolated in small refuge areas on promontories or peninsulas, or in valleys between mountain ranges, in cold periods; or on mountains and uplands when lowland conditions became unsuitable during hot periods. These separated populations, isolated for long periods, developed their own peculiarities of appearance and structure. When conditions reunited such divided populations, some might begin to interbreed again in spite of differences and, where we can recognize such populations, we usually call them subspecies or geographical races. In other instances, however, the differences had become so great that the populations no longer recognized each other and behaved as new and separate species.

Australia is not affected directly by glaciation except on the highlands of the south-eastern corner. It has an old, worn-down landscape with few areas of high ground, except at this south-eastern end of the Great Dividing Range with a high point of 2208 metres (7263 feet). These Pleistocene

Above: *The massive bill of the Black Cockatoo* Calyptorhynchus funereus *can splinter wood and is used for extracting seeds from cones and burrowing grubs from timber.*

Left: *Inconspicuous at rest, the long skin pouch of the lower bill and throat of the Australian Pelican* Pelecanus perspicillatus *extends as a great scoop when it is fishing.*
Below: *Fleshy flanges that expand the tip give the bill of the Pink-eared Duck* Malacorhynchus membranaceus *a drooping look.*

alternations of climate affected it with periods of wetter and cooler conditions followed by hotter and drier conditions; and, in the later part of the Pleistocene, more arid conditions predominated for longer periods. These wet and dry cycles do not coincide neatly with the glacial and interglacial periods at the poles, differing from some regions to others; and, contrary to expectation, desert areas were drier when it was cold elsewhere, wetter when it was warmer.

During the wetter periods, woodland and forest was much more widespread, and there was water in the rivers and lakes although some lakes were salty. In drier periods, the greater part of the land became semidesert or desert, with trees and moist grassland limited to a few regions, usually on higher ground around the coasts, while rivers became dry creeks and lakes turned to dust or salt pans.

There is increasing evidence of birds that were lost during these dry periods. The inland lakes had supported a population of the Greater Flamingo *Phoenicopterus ruber* which still occurs elsewhere in the world, as well as a giant flamingo and a dwarf species which are now extinct. There were also the dromornithids, a family of great, blunt-billed, emu-like birds, many of which were substantially bigger

Top left: *The plumage pattern of the Crested Shrike-tit* Falcunculus frontatus *shows its whistler affinities in spite of a massive bark-tearing bill of parrot-like proportions.*

Centre left: *The Emu* Dromaius novaehollandiae *is one of Australia's earliest species, at home in open country of all kinds.*

Bottom left and right: *The Squatter Pigeon* Geophaps scripta *of the north-east and Partridge Pigeon G. smithii of the north-west are examples of the Australian ground pigeons. Both inhabit grassy woodlands and are probably of similar origin but have evolved into separate species after isolation by drier country.*

Above: *The little Red-browed finches* Emblema temporalis, *here seen drinking, feed on open ground in bushy places. They strongly resemble some African waxbill species.*

than emus, and all of them more heavily built. They had ranged across Australia for perhaps 30 million years but became extinct during the late Pleistocene. There are probably many more that have been lost, but smaller birds are difficult to identify from the bones that are found in caves or buried in the ground. They may resemble those of present-day species, and it is only the oddities, such as the Giant Megapode, twice the size of a Mallee Fowl *Leipoa ocellata*, that are quickly recognized.

New Guinea is a recently formed land. At the beginning of the Pleistocene, it was little more than a chain of islands but, very gradually, it was forced up to its present height, with steep new mountain ranges that caught the rains and grew dense forest. When the forest birds of Australia were driven into the coastal regions or were killed off by the aridity of the Pleistocene periods, some took refuge in New Guinea. In fact, the forest birdlife of New Guinea may be derived from that of Australia in earlier times, and may provide clues to some of the birds that are no longer found in Australia.

In wetter periods, when conditions were more favourable for plant growth, some New Guinea birds were able to re-invade Australia. Birds can make such movements more readily because of their powers of flight, but the to-and-fro movements of all kinds of living things between Australia and New Guinea were aided by the effects of the Ice Ages.

During the colder periods when ice accumulated as great masses, not only at the poles but on many continents, less water returned to the oceans and, in these periods, sea-level fell. It has been estimated that the fall in level during the coldest periods were between 80 and 150 metres (260 to 495 feet) below the present level. In very warm periods, sea-level probably rose higher than it is today. With these large drops in sea-level, Australia would have been joined to New Guinea and Tasmania as a single land mass. The shallowest part of the Torres Straits, between Cape York and New Guinea, is only about 10 metres (33 feet) deep and a land bridge could have persisted here for a long time even after sea-levels rose again. The depth of water between Tasmania and Australia, however, reaches 50 metres (165 feet) at the moment and the two lands would have separated sooner and for longer periods.

These repeated fragmentations and re-unitings of bird populations, as well as movements into areas that became available as conditions changed, produced patterns that can be recognized in the present-day distribution of species. These patterns recur in different groups, indicating a common history. At times, the patterns help us to understand how Australia has acquired its present birdlife.

Over the longer term, Australia's climate was arid during the last glacial period of the Pleistocene, became wetter afterwards, but over the last thousands of years has become drier again. In dry periods, the centre of Australia becomes very arid, the dry conditions extending virtually to the sea on either side of the Hamersley Ranges in the west, and the

Left and above: *The solidly built Crimson Finch* Neochmia phaeton *is a northern species of tall waterside canegrass and Pandanus, and similar vegetation; it builds a domed grass nest in tall grass, trees, or on houses. The two central birds here are females. The male has white flank specks like those of Crimson Firefinches of Africa.*

Great Australian Bight in the south. In such severely dry conditions, birds needing trees or bushes and some moisture have been forced into isolated refuges. If they stay in such areas for long periods, they become adapted to local conditions, and these adaptations may either help or limit their subsequent spread when conditions improve. The refuges tended to form a ring around the coastal areas.

Species-rings are typical of a number of groups, and the red-shouldered blue wren exemplifies a complete ring with seven distinct forms involved, even though not all are currently regarded as full species. Females are grey-blue in northern forms, otherwise brown; males differ subtly. The Variegated Wren *Malurus lamberti* with a black-breasted male is found on the south-east side of the Great Dividing Range. Down in the moister south-west corner is the Red-winged Wren *M. elegans* with its dark blue breast. In the Kimberleys of the north-west, the White-flanked Wren *M. dulcis* has a black-breasted male, while the female has a chestnut eye-patch; in Arnhem Land the male is similar but the female has a white eye-patch. The Lovely Wren *M. amabilis* of Cape York is deeper blue in both sexes. In the south, probably originating from the Eyre Peninsula, the Blue-breasted Wren *M. pulcherrimus*, with a blue-breasted male, is adapted to drier mallee (eucalyptus scrub) and heath conditions, and has spread across to the west coast north of the Red-winged Wren's range. Finally, the Purple-backed Wren *M. assimilis*, another black-breasted species, seems to have originated from a western refuge, possibly the Hamersley region. This bird is adapted to the driest conditions, and consequently it has spread back across the whole central dry region of Australia not occupied by the others; this has made its refuge more difficult to guess at, and completes the recolonization of Australia by this ring of separate species.

The tree-clambering Sittella *Neositta chrysoptera* has a ring of five forms: with black cap and orange wingbar in the south-west; black cap and white wingbar in the north-west;

Above: *The Beautiful Firetail* Emblema bella *is an unobtrusive grassfinch of dense vegetation. It is quite drab in appearance, noticeable only when males are calling from high perches.*

Below: *The Variegated Wren* Malurus lamberti *is one of the red-shouldered wrens. Deep blue on back and nape in eclipse, males resemble the brown females but lack a chestnut eye patch.*

black cap, white wingbar, and bodystreaking in the north-east; white head and orange wingbar in the mid-east of the Dividing Range; and grey head and orange wingbar in the south-east. The distribution is similar to that of the red-shouldered wren but these forms meet and interbreed freely and are, therefore, regarded as subspecies of a single species.

The brown treecreepers, *Climacteris* species, have a mixed pattern, with one species in the south-west, one in the north-west, and one through the eastern side of Australia; but the latter two are further separated into two distinct local sub-species.

The rosella parrots show a more complex situation. The pale-cheeked species show a ring, with the small, yellow-cheeked Western Rosella *Platycercus icterotis* in the south-west, the dark-crowned Northern Rosella *P. venustus* in the north-west, the Pale-headed Rosella *P. adscitus* in the north-east, and the gaudy Eastern Rosella *P. eximius* in the south-east. Superimposed on this, down the eastern side, is another replacement pattern of blue-cheeked rosellas, from the Crimson Rosella *P. elegans*, through the Adelaide Rosella *P. adelaidae* and Yellow Rosella *P. flaveolus* of the south-east, to the Green Rosella *P. caledonicus* of Tasmania.

These variations are due to recurrent changes over a long period, of which we see only the latest results and must guess the earlier stages. Other patterns also recur. During wetter periods, Lake Eyre and other lakes of central Australia filled, and the associated creeks were surrounded by a lot of vegetation. Some birds, which preferred arid conditions and which lived in the central region, divided into separate eastern and western populations. For example, there are two species of wedgebills which differ slightly in plumage and more distinctly in voice. The latter characteristic is the most useful, and they have been recognized as the Chiming Wedgebill *Psophodes occidentalis* of the dry west, and the Chirruping Wedgebill *P. cristatus* of the dry east. Conversely, the more abundant vegetation of wetter periods

Below: *The strong-footed, climbing ability of the Sittella* Neositta chrysoptera *can be seen here. Its nest is built into a fork and is finely camouflaged with bark.*
Above: *When perched beside the nest cavity, the Brown Treecreeper* Climacteris picumnus *shows little evidence of its specialized habit of climbing up tree trunks and branches.*
Below right: *This male Western Rosella* Platycercus icterotis *is one of the smaller and brighter of the pale-cheeked species.*

allowed some birds to move between east and west and, when dry periods occurred, separated pairs of tree-haunting species were formed. The Port Lincoln Parrot *Barnardius zonarius* of south-western woodland has a corresponding species, the Mallee Ringneck *B. barnardi*, in the drier open woodland of the east.

In addition to these speciation patterns, repeated invasions followed by the evolution of new species helped to create more complex avifaunas in some areas. Recurrent incidents of this kind occurred throughout the Cape York peninsula as a result of invasion from New Guinea, and demonstrate typical patterns. An early invader of the forest east of the Dividing Range may change over time to become a separate species, after which its range may be overlapped and shared by a later invasion of birds of the same original stock. Such invasions probably occurred in successive wetter periods of the Pleistocene. The honeyeaters provide examples of this. One instance involves what appears to be a triple invasion. All three birds are similar; drab olive-brown with a yellow cheek-patch which is slightly different in each type. The iris of the eye is bluish in the first and last, brown in the other bird, and the bills progressively longer and thinner; although the last is nearest the ancestral form.

The first was Lewin's Honeyeater *Meliphaga lewini* which extends through wetter forest right down to the south-east. The second from this stock, the Yellow-spotted Honeyeater *M. notata* now occurs in rainforest down the eastern side of Cape York and south to Mackay, overlapping in the south of its range with the northern end of that of Lewin's Honeyeater. The third species, the Graceful Honeyeater *M. gracilis* is still present in New Guinea. In Australia it has occupied rainforest in eastern Cape York, in part overlapping in range with the other two, and has been present long enough to be regarded as a separate subspecies to its New Guinea stock. All three are difficult to separate in the wild, but have differences of voice. Because of the various small differences in characteristics and in precise choice of habitat, they are able to co-exist

Top: *The vivid plumage pattern of the male Crimson Rosella* Platycercus elegans *contrasts sharply with its surroundings and makes it the most conspicuous of the blue-cheeked rosellas.*

Above: *The Chiming Wedgebill* Psophodes occidentalis *is a skulker known from its monotonous descending song phrase.*

Below left: *The Port Lincoln Parrot* Barnardius zonarius *of the south-west is a bird of trees and roadsides. It is yellow chested in the corn belt, but green fronted on south-western coasts.*

Below right: *The Mallee Ringneck* B. barnardi *is the Port Lincoln Parrot's paler counterpart in eastern Australia.*

Above: *Lewin's Honeyeater* Meliphaga lewini *of eastern wet forest is closely related to the Yellow-spotted Honeyeater on page 6.*

Right: *In the King Quail* Excalfactoria chinensis, *the darker, chestnut-bellied male differs strikingly from the female.*

Below right: *The Willy Wagtail* Rhipidura leucophrys, *a long-legged and ground-feeding fantail flycatcher, coats and binds its nest tightly with spiders' webs.*

During the periods of isolation the species that evolved here have become adapted to different types of vegetation and different climates, and so helped to fill the varying habitats available for birds throughout the continent as a whole. It is possible to identify some invaders that became mainly adapted to the drier areas where there was a lack of competing species. They tend to have become larger, duller, and browner in colour. Examples are scattered among the bird families, including the Malleefowl *Leipoa ocellata,* among the megapodes, and the Black-eared Cuckoo *Chrysococcyx osculans* among the little glossy cuckoos. The Brown Quail *Synoicus australis* seems to be a large, female-coloured form of the King Quail *Excalfactoria chinensis.* The latter has invaded again more recently, hardly differing from others in the oriental region, and still retaining the bright colours of the male.

Another tendency among birds colonizing the open parts of Australia is towards terrestrialism. The existence of ground-living, gamebird-like pigeons has already been mentioned. Another example can be seen in the Willie Wagtail *Rhipidura leucophrys,* a fantail that has left the trees to become a longer-legged bird spending more time on the ground, flushing out insects with lateral swings of the tail.

With this ebb and flow of birds over long periods of climatic change, with periodic invasions, and with the formation of new species in isolation, Australia has acquired a bird fauna adapted to almost all the habitats it can offer. The species are adapted to co-exist with others by exploiting differences in what the environment can offer in food sources, nest sites, and other basic needs. The species found in any particular area depend on the habitats available.

The main habitats are determined by vegetation and, in Australia, this is arranged roughly in belts around an arid centre that is nearer the western side of the country. The true deserts are areas of shifting sands or stony gibber (boulder) plains, but there are large stretches of spiny hummocks of spinifex grasses or thinly scattered mulga scrub. In better areas bordering these are stretches of tussocky Mitchell grass and the low shrubby growth of saltbush and bluebush. In less dry but poor areas, eucalypts grow as dwarfed, multi-stemmed trees to form the mallee zone in southern parts. Elsewhere, grassland gives way to open woodland.

Along the northern regions, down the eastern Great Dividing Range zone and in the south-west of Australia, there is more humid woodland – tropical and temperate. In wetter places on the eastern side, and in the extreme south-west, dry eucalypt forest grades into wet eucalypt forest. Where the moist, onshore winds meet the eastern side of the Great Dividing Range, there are patches of dense rainforest, while the monsoons create similar patches of forest from the western Gulf of Carpentaria to the Kimberleys. Finally, the mangroves form a woodland belt extending into the shallow seas around the northern half of Australia from Shark Bay to New South Wales.

Areas of poor soil with higher rainfall produce heathland in places around the coastal regions. These have a low, scrubby plant and bush growth, but one which is rich in flowering plants. There is some alpine heath on the higher mountains of the south-east and in Tasmania, but there are not enough areas at higher altitudes to support a special montane-type bird fauna.

Other important bird habitats are associated with water. The wetlands range from temporary creeks and inland lakes which may be wet or dry depending on the rains, to the more permanent rivers and streams, the swamps, and coastal lakes and lagoons. Finally, there is the sea coast, a rich source of food for birds specialized to exploit it. In some places, especially on islands, it offers suitable nest sites for those species that spend most of their time at sea.

In the chapters that follow these various habitats are examined to see what kinds of birds occur and how they are adapted to them.

2
Living With People:
Semi-Natural Areas

For anyone who wishes instantly to indicate an Australian setting on radio or film it is all too often thought adequate to put into the background somewhere the crazy cackling of a Kookaburra. For a sound that might suggest a suburban background, however, but is beautifully and unmistakably Australian, there is a more musical call. This is a series of deep melodious notes of slightly varying pitch and of a surprising resonance; the notes are uttered as groups of calls, overlapping in ragged succession with pauses between. They have been compared to the notes of an organ, and come from a small group of crow-like pied birds perched in a tree. It is the territorial chorus of the Australian Magpie *Gymnorhina tibicens*. The species actually occurs throughout most of Australia, and its basic needs are relatively simple – open grassy places on which to feed, scattered trees in which to nest, and a ready supply of water. The accidental provision of these brings one of the country's finer singers into the urban setting.

There is probably no area in Australia untouched by human activity; this includes the introduction of grazing animals such as sheep, cattle, goats, camels, pigs, and buffalos or the infamous rabbit. When carefully examined, the 'Great Untouched Outback' turns out to be something of a myth. In most instances, however, what human activity has done there is to modify the vegetation from one type to another, by overgrazing and selective feeding. The real test for adaptability faces birds in the areas most intensely modified by human settlement; from towns, through suburbs, to the areas of orchards, cultivation, and small paddocks that spread at the periphery.

The Magpies are more typical of outer areas, or the parks golfcourses, and sports fields of inner suburbs. They are black birds with white or mottled patches on back, wings, and tail area. The stout, tapering bill is light blue with a black tip. Superficially crow-like, they are actually members of the butcherbird family, unrelated to the magpies of other parts of the world. Red-irised eyes show up in a black head. There are northern, western, and eastern subspecies, differing in the extent of white on the plumage. Older males have most white on the back, while females and young are mottled.

Australian Magpies have evolved a complex social behaviour. They form small groups, the more successful of which have dominant males which may mate with several females, each of which nests separately. Additional males help to defend a communal territory against other groups,

Left: Some homes in the south-east are fortunate in that the Superb Blue Wren Malurus cyaneus *seems to regard gardens and parks as slightly different kinds of heaths and woodland.*

and the carolling calls are a group's announcement of territorial ownership. They dig and probe for insects, mainly on open ground. They are fine additions to an area, but unfortunately the defence of the nest includes swooping down and pecking at potential predators. With the use of parks and suburbs for nesting, innocent passersby may be dive-bombed by angry birds, and may suffer painful jabs on the scalp. Such incidents tend to lead to demands for the birds to be shot. The whole problem of how closely birds may live with humans depends on agreed levels of tolerance that are sometimes strained.

Even Magpies do not adapt to areas such as city centres. These represent new and alien surroundings for the birds which once inhabited the area. They have tended to be almost devoid of birdlife; the people who have created them in Australia, certainly in the recent past, have usually come from other countries and continents. Lovely as the appearance and voices of Australian birds may be, these people were homesick for familiar sounds of their past, and so they imported and naturalized the birds of their place of origin. Fortunately, perhaps, most of these attempts were unsuccessful but, where a new and alien (to indigenous birds) habitat had been created by human settlement, this might be the one to which the imported bird was already adapted and it could then take over that area successfully. The Domestic Pigeon, the tame form of the Rock Dove *Columba livia*, is just such a successful invader. It differs from most pigeons in its nesting needs. Instead of living as scattered pairs nesting in trees, its natural tendency is to nest in colonies on the ledges and in the recesses of caves and sheltered rocky places. For this bird, cities are endless rocky gullies with many ledges, recesses, and cave-like structures, some of which are suitable for nesting. From these it can fly out daily in search of food, sometimes at a considerable distance.

The Pigeon has learned to investigate possible food items thrown down by humans and to take artificial foods, such as bread, as well as using natural plants and seeds of all kinds. Ledges on buildings, interiors of deserted buildings, roof supports of railway terminuses, and similar structures, as well as girders and ledges on the undersides of bridges are all typical nest colony sites. A thin twig platform is balanced on a site, later plastered down inadvertently with droppings, and constantly re-used. The subdued throaty cooing, and the loud, quick wingflaps of the male before he displays in a level glide, are common signs of at least attempted breeding.

The typical plumage in both sexes is ashy grey, darker on the purple-glossed neck and tail tip, and with two black wingbars and a white lower back. Domestic forms have been produced in which the normal colour has become increasingly dark-spotted or wholly replaced by blue-black, or in

This Australian Magpie Gymnorhina tibicens, *nesting in a tree-fern, shows the stout, tapering, ground-probing bill. The female has the tasks of building, incubating, and feeding the young.*

which the whole bird is a chestnut-brown colour. Such plumages as these may be partly or wholly replaced by white. Selective breeding by humans has led to this range of colours, but the more conspicuous individuals are more likely to be noticed and killed by predators such as the Peregrine Falcon *Falco peregrinus*.

This wide-ranging circumpolar falcon is thinly distributed through Australia. It is a large, compact, chunky falcon with long, tapering wings. It flies fast and dives on its prey, rocketing down with wings half closed and the big, strong feet held close to the body. The impact when it strikes drives the big curved talons on its feet into its prey, killing it in the air or knocking it to the ground. The Peregrine seems particularly partial to Pigeons and, for this reason, is disliked by Pigeon racers who blame it for any losses; the bird will, in fact, take a range of prey from Galahs to honeyeaters.

It is a dark, blue-grey bird with darker barrings, and white on the underside with fine black bars; the young are browner. The crown and sides of the head are black, and there is a rim of bare yellow skin around the big dark eyes. Somehow, this falcon seems to appear from nowhere at great speed, stoop on its prey, and disappear again just as fast. It will rest on tall buildings, but needs an undisturbed nesting site; in fact, it does not make a nest as such but makes use of a ledge of a rock outcrop, or the large tree-nest of some other bird.

Another immigrant that shares town life is the House Sparrow *Passer domesticus*. Introduced in the mid-nineteenth century, it has spread through eastern Australia; it is so closely linked with human settlement, however, that by keeping a watch on the smaller outstations, it has been possible to prevent it spreading to the west. It needs a raised nest site and will live in colonies; and it feeds mainly on the ground, usually taking seeds but prepared to investigate possible new foods. It exploits human activity, becoming fairly tame, but surviving by never becoming too trusting. Buildings often provide the House Sparrow with sheltered sites and crevices for nests, which may be little more than untidy masses of grass and feathers. If forced to, it is perfectly capable of building a neat, rounded nest with a side

entrance in a twiggy bush or tree. The call of the male as he advertises possession of the nest is a noisy, chirping. In display, he hops around chirping frantically, with drooped wings, cocked tail, and head tilted back to show the black throat bib.

The House Sparrow's stout bill is designed to deal with seeds but these adaptable little birds will take buds and berries, and occasionally flowers. When there are young in the nest, both parents begin avidly searching plants and trees for the small insects that the young need. The more built-up and alien parts of cities are dominated by these introduced birds. Moving to the more open suburbs with gardens, lawns, shrubs, and scattered trees, as well as the more extensive parkland, the native birds begin to appear, but they still share their environment with other well-established immigrants.

The only native starling in Australia is the green-glossed and red-eyed Shining Starling *Aplonis metallica* of the Queensland rainforests; but two species that were introduced into towns in the mid-nineteenth century still survive. Of the two, the Common Myna *Acridotheres tristis*, which originated from India, is slightly larger and more sturdily built. It is warm brown in colour with a blackish head and a bare yellow patch behind the eye. The bill is short and stoutish, and bristly feathers give it a high forehead. It usually appears in pairs or in family parties, swaggering around on the ground in open places and scavenging for food. When it flies, the rather rounded wings show a large white patch on the dark feathers, conspicuous at a distance.

The Common Myna uses a mixture of low-pitched call-notes, wheezy whistles, and subdued rattling. It is at its noisiest when numbers gather in communal roosts in trees or in some sheltered site, with a rising volume of raucous and scolding notes as they defend a chosen perch. It eats mainly fruit and insects and is confined largely to the vicinity of larger eastern towns, although it is present inland in south

Queensland and in the sugarcane country of the north-east. It seems closely tied to human settlement and agriculture, where its raids on fruit may make it a pest. It builds an untidy nest in a tree hole or in a cavity or crevice on some part of a building.

The Common Starling *Sturnus vulgaris*, imported from Europe, has fared rather better. It has a more slender, upright stance and has blackish, purple-glossed plumage. After the moult, this is spangled with pale tips that wear off through the breeding season. Its head is more slender and the bill is longer and more tapering. In addition to sharing the Common Myna's fondness for fruit and readiness to investigate household scraps and rubbish, and even to eat seed, it is adept at eating insects. It probes in turf, soft soil, and vegetation with its bill which it will thrust well in and then open slightly, the upper and lower mandibles forcing the material apart while the eyes, close-set at the base of the bill, squint along the bill to see if food is present. This feeding method may give it an advantage over the Myna.

The Starling often feeds in open spaces, usually gathering in social groups even when nesting. At other times, it may assemble in huge flocks, particularly when roosting, and the flocks may perform spectacular mass-manoeuvres before settling for the night. The birds roost in trees, reedbeds, and even on city buildings. The dirt and damage caused by the roosts make the Starling unpopular, as do its raids on soft fruit crops.

Its cup nest is hidden in a hole in a tree or building, and it has a habit of squeezing under the roofs of houses. It advertises its presence by singing, its head and throat feathers spikily erected, uttering a weird succession of whistles, squeaks, throaty bubbling and clicking notes. It has spread through the south-east, and appears to have begun extending its range north and west, in spite of efforts to control it.

One problem that arises with both the last two species is their large local populations and their use of tree holes. Eucalypt trees rot easily in the heartwood, and hollow branches and cavities are relatively common. Many native Australian birds rely on such holes for successful nesting. Mynas and Starlings take over a large number of these holes. The pair waits patiently until the other occupying species leaves for a moment and then they move in, filling the hole with nest material. Once they are in possession, the original owners do not appear to put up a fight, however well established they were. Amazingly enough, even parrots such as rosellas will allow themselves to be ousted in this fashion; although one good bite from a parrot's bill would have settled the argument. In this respect, birds such as Mynas and Starlings are probably doing more harm environmentally than in their raids on orchards and crops.

Below: *As it is a cave pigeon, the Rock Dove* Columba livia *is better adapted to using buildings than Australia's native pigeons, and this gives it an advantage in urban areas.*

Bottom left: *The male House Sparrow* Passer domesticus, *here carrying food, joins in nest building and feeding young.*
Bottom right: *This Common Myna* Acridotheres tristis *landing at the nest shows the typical characteristics, including the large white patch on the wing.*

It is probably the hollow trees that have maintained the presence in towns of two predatory birds which are widespread throughout Australia and which are unlikely to tolerate any approach from starlings. One is the Boobook Owl *Ninox novaeseelandiae*. Only slightly smaller than a Magpie, it is brown with white spots, with staring, yellow-irised eyes under a pair of big white eyebrows that meet above the bill. It feeds on mice and small birds, and will also catch night-flying moths which, in towns, it may find around street lights. It is named after its low-pitched *boo-book* hoot. It nests in a tree-hole, and roosts by day either in a hole or huddled in dense foliage. It is disliked by small birds which mob it noisily if they find it. A party of excited and noisy honeyeaters taking it in turn to peer into a hollow broken branch of a tree may reveal the daytime hiding place of a concealed owl. In addition to its occurrence in settled areas with trees, this owl can be found in any region of the country

Previous pages – left: *The Peregrine Falcon* Falco peregrinus *could, in theory, nest on ledges or on the roofs of tall buildings, but this bird dislikes disturbance and prefers to occupy rock ledges. This female is using the large hollow top of a broken-off tree trunk.*
Previous pages – right: *The partly worn spring plumage of the Starling* Sturnus vulgaris *shows the glossy colours. At a distance, it becomes a blackish bird with an upright bustling walk.*
Below: *Caught in the beam of a flashlight, this Boobook Owl* Ninox novaeseelandiae *shows the expanded pupils of a bird using all the available light for seeing its prey. The legs are strong; the outer toe is turned backwards.*

where suitable trees are present.

The other species, the Nankeen Kestrel *Falco cenchroides*, is a daytime hunter. This is a small, sandy brown falcon with a whitish underside. It is a comparatively weak raptor and is usually seen hovering, hanging in one place before dropping on to its prey. In this manoeuvre, the head remains fixed on one spot, however much body, wings, and tail may twist and adjust; this helps it take aim before swooping. Its food may be a mouse, lizard, or bird, or just an insect for which all that effort seems rather wasted. In addition to using tree holes and hollows, it may nest on ledges or on the roofs of buildings or rock ledges; it may also use old nests of other birds. Like other falcons, it does not collect nest material. Like the Rock Dove, it seems to see towns as a collection of rocky cliffs; and House Sparrows acceptable food. It is an adaptable bird, and its range extends from urban areas right out to open woodland and the more scattered trees on arid inland areas.

Suburban nest-hole problems have not driven parrots away altogether. In the south-east, one of the gaudiest rosellas, the Eastern Rosella *Platycercus eximius*, occurs in roadside trees, around paddocks and orchards, and into parks and gardens. It manages to display all the primary colours in its plumage: red head and breast; yellow belly; green and blue wings and tail; the whole offset by white cheeks and black on the mantle and wings. It searches on the ground and in shrubs and trees for seeds but the bird will also take fruit, berries, nectar, and buds. It moves in a fast dipping flight with a high-pitched *pink-pink* call; the Eastern Rosella uses a rising triple-note piping to maintain contact. Its nest hole may be quite low, and this parrot can be

Above: *These half-fledged young of the Nankeen Kestrel* Falco cenchroides *in their unlined nest hollow already show the adult-type colouring, the big, keen eyes, and the falcon feet.*

Below: *The Green Rosella* Platycercus caledonicus *of Tasmania is a larger, less gaudy member of the blue-cheeked rosellas.*

Above: *The territory-holding parties of Superb Blue Wrens* Malurus cyaneus *usually show at least one full-plumaged male like this.*

Below: *The angle of wall and roof offers an artificial site where a Welcome Swallow* Hirundo neoxena *can glue its mud nest.*

persuaded to use a nestbox.

In winter the Eastern Rosella may be joined by the equally striking crimson-and-blue Crimson Rosella *P. elegans*; the younger birds are green with red and blue markings. It moves into parks and gardens and, as well as eating native berries, it takes exotic fruits such as hawthorn. Both species search road margins for seed and grit and may be killed by traffic.

In Tasmania it is the Green Rosella – *P. caledonicus*, which actually has a yellow head and body, red forehead, and blue cheeks – that has moved into orchards, parks, and the wooded edges of towns. It is a larger bird with a more level flight pattern. Like the others, it has abrupt high-pitched calls when on the move, but becomes very silent and unobtrusive when feeding; and the bright plumage colours can be surprisingly inconspicuous among trees laden with ripe fruit.

In south-western Australia, the Port Lincoln Parrot *Barnardius zonarius* is the one most likely to occur in agricultural areas, orchards, and parks. Its trisyllabic or disyllabic call has given it the alternative name of Twenty-eight Parrot.

Relatively few birds rely on human architecture for nest-sites. One obvious exception is the Welcome Swallow. This needs a site on which it can fix its cup nest of mud pellets – under an overhang in a cave-like recess. In the wild, it must use a cave, or a site provided by a hollow or fallen tree. Houses, bridges, culverts, and mineshafts all provide acceptable alternatives, and a sloping roof support of a porch, veranda, or open garage, or an old shed with a broken door, are ideal.

The bird circles and skims around buildings and open spaces, and low over dams or other areas of water, catching insects as it goes. Its exuberant, twittering song is usually sung from an overhead wire or, more rarely, from a thin bare twig. The carefully built-up cup of mud pellets and stems

Above: *The Blackbird* Turdus merula *sings his lazy musical song as he moves around his territory as well as from a song post.*
Below: *This vigorous, musical, and strong-billed songster, the Grey Shrike-thrush* Colluricincla harmonica *has extended its range from woodland and scrub to parks and gardens.*
Right: *The Eastern Rosella* Platycercus eximius, *here at a tree nest-hole, shows its bright colours in the roadside trees, orchards, and gardens of the south-east.*

may be stuck to near-vertical surfaces and is lined with feathers. Snatching insects from the air, the birds are happiest where cattle or similar stock attract flies, or near water, but, given open areas for hunting and a nest site that they can return to year after year, they manage very well. The Welcome Swallow occurs throughout southern and eastern Australia, and eastern birds show some northward migration in winter.

The closest some other birds come to buildings is to nest in shrubs or vines growing up against them. Most typical of these are probably the thrush-like birds. One is a true thrush and an introduced species. The European Blackbird *Turdus merula*, first introduced in the mid-nineteenth century, has spread throughout the better vegetated parts of the south-east. It was almost certainly brought in for its song which is so familiar around British homes. The male has a rather leisurely, low-pitched song phrase, varying between individuals, and often musical enough to be whistled, but tending to end on a harsh note. It usually sings from a tree or roof-top perch. The Blackbird feeds on the ground where it often carries the longish tail in a slightly raised position. The bird hunts for small creatures, at times scratching in leaf litter; and it will also take ripe fruit. The male is black with a yellow bill and thin eye-rim; the female is dull brown.

The Blackbird's nest is a bulky cup with some mud mixed into the plant material. It is tucked into a hidden tree or shrub fork, or a recess, or in a shrub or climber against the wall of a building. The Blackbird is an excitable species and, with breeding birds in earshot, we become accustomed to the subdued *quilp* and *chook* calls, and the wilder screeching outbursts of alarm.

The Australian native equivalent is the Grey Shrike-thrush *Colluricincla harmonica*. This widespread species is similar in size to the Blackbird but its bill is stouter and blunter tipped, and has a small hook at the end of the upper mandible. It is mainly ashy grey in colour but has eastern,

Above: *In its bold colours, the introduced European Goldfinch* Carduelis carduelis *can match many of the native grassfinches.* Below: *It was probably a tolerance of humans at its place of origin that gave the introduced Spotted Dove* Streptopelia chinensis *the advantage over similar native pigeons.*

western, and northern forms, the latter two birds being buff bellied and browner respectively. Young birds have darkish breast streaks and a reddish eyestripe. The Grey Shrike thrush has a stronger bill than the Blackbird and is a more vigorous feeder, taking also small frogs, lizards, and even eggs and nestlings, or small mammals. It hunts along the branches and trunks of trees as well as on the ground. It has loud, abrupt, ringing call notes. The male's song is a variable, short song phrase; it is clear, melodious, and carries a long way. It usually consists of two to five repeated notes, ending with a rising double-note – *pur, pur, pur, quee-yule* or *pip, pip, hoo-ee*. The large cup nest is usually tucked into thick, leafy cover or in a sheltered recess such as a shallow tree cavity or broken stump. In gardens, it may be found in creeping plants on a wall, behind a pipe, or in an open shed or veranda.

For small birds investigating the places where people live, the gardens and vegetation probably resemble most nearly heathland or some type of open savanna woodland. Open ground, grassy or bare and with spaced plants, is mixed with scattered groups of shrubs, which are often rich in flowers and berries, and with some trees. Houses may be no more relevant than a heap of fallen rocks. Relatively few small songbirds have adapted fully to these areas, and the southeast is fortunate that its endemic blue wren has found the mixture of open ground and low bushy cover ideal for its purposes. This is the Superb Wren *Malurus cyaneus*. The female is sandy brown in colour with a reddish eye-patch; but the male has silvery blue cheeks, crown, and back, and a deep blue breast, all bordered with jet black. Both have the slender blue tail, as long again as the rest of the bird and usually carried almost erect.

Like many Australian birds, this species lives in social groups consisting of a dominant pair and a small number of helpers, mostly young males. These helpers will assist in the nesting by taking part in nest building, and care and feeding of the young. Ultimately, some helpers may hope to replace the older, dominant birds. The whole group moves around a territory which is defended against other groups. They spread out over open ground, hunting insects and keeping in touch with one another with small *prit-prit* calls. The dominant male and female also use a thin, high-pitched reeling song phrase. When alarmed they retreat into bushy cover. Superb Wrens roost on a perch, huddling together to form a many tailed feather ball. The nest is domed, with an entrance in the side. It is hidden in the thicker growth of a shrub or tree. The introduced blackberry is favoured where it is available as a good support and as a deterrent to predators.

Another small bird of bushes and grass in eastern Australia is the little Red-browed Finch. Like the blue wren, it builds a domed nest in a bush. It breeds as separate pairs, but it is a highly sociable species. Small parties or flocks composed of pairs or family parties feed on lawns and in the open, taking small seeds, and keeping up small, high-pitched *see-see* calls. They tend frequently to twitch the tail sideways, revealing the scarlet rump, which is also conspicuous when they retreat to cover in bouncy flight. When displaying to its mate, the male Finch has an odd posture, stretching up rigidly with a long grass stem held above him, one end in his bill, while he bounces up and down in a series of vigorous jerks.

In general, Australian seed eaters have not exploited human settlements, and introduced birds have established themselves. The European Goldfinch *Carduelis carduelis*, a little smaller than a sparrow, has found a place in the weedy margins of roads and farmland, in orchards, and in the neglected corners of suburbs. In the last 100 years, it has spread in the settled south-east. The distinctive twangy, twittering calls, dancing flight, and black-and-yellow wings attract attention to it. At closer quarters, the scarlet face on the black-and-white head can be seen. It tends to feed cling-

Below: *The tiny Grey-breasted White-eye* Zosterops lateralis *suspends its fragile cup nest between twigs, the need for insects for nestlings diverting its attention from soft fruits.*

Below: *The slender bill of the Eastern Spinebill* Acanthorhynchus tenuirostris *helps it probe into long flowers such as this Grevillea for nectar, and to seek hidden insects.*

ing to seeding plants and grasses, sometimes fluttering as it extracts seeds. The nest is a cup of fine material with a soft lining, built in the fork of a shrub or tree.

The more heavily built Greenfinch *C. chloris*, also introduced in the last century, has not spread quite as far. The male is dull green with yellow on its wings and tail; the female is olive brown. The bird feeds on larger seeds, mainly taken from the ground. It has a musical twittering song and a twisting aerial display flight, but more often it uses a long harsh *dweezsh* note instead, monotonously repeated from a perch. It also builds a thick cup nest in a shrub or tree.

The other seed-eating birds that might have moved into these new areas are the pigeons but once again, it was an immigrant that has been successful. The Spotted Dove *Streptopelia chinensis* is an introduction from the east; it is a little smaller and more slender than a Rock Dove and has a longer tail. It feeds on the ground but rests and nests in trees. Exceptionally, it will nest on ledges of buildings. It is a brown-mottled bird with a pinkish breast and grey head; there is a big black patch spotted with white on the back and sides of the neck. Its call is a repeated clear *coo-oo croo* or slight variants, with a more rapid cooing accompanying a quick bowing display by the male. It advertises itself in an upward flight with loud wingbeats followed by a spiralling, downward glide with spread wings and tail. Its readiness to nest in tall shrubs or trees of gardens, and to seek food around buildings, tolerating human beings, have helped its success. It occurs mainly throughout areas of denser human settlement in the east and south, from Queensland to Western Australia. It shares the south-west with a similar but smaller species, the Senegal Dove *Streptopelia senegalensis*, introduced from North Africa. This is a bird of similar habits. It is sandy coloured with blue-grey wings and with darker mottling on the throat, most obvious when that is

Below: *The Western Spinebill* Acanthorhynchus superciliosus *is more boldly patterned than the eastern bird. It has the same flower-probing and insect-hunting habits as its eastern cousin, and these habits also bring it into gardens.*
Above: *The nest of the Yellow-faced Honeyeater* Lichenostomus chrysops *is very deep and well woven for a honeyeater.*
Right: *The Red Wattlebirds* Anthochaera carunculata, *with their odd, harsh calls, will move in search of nectar-bearing flowers, such as this Banksia, probing with narrow curved bill.*

inflated during cooing. It has a softer and more bubbling call that gives this introduced species the alternative name of Laughing Dove.

The little Grey-breasted White-eye with its needle-sharp bill can find insects anywhere in trees or bushes, but is drawn to human settlements by the prospect of berries and soft fruits on which it feeds avidly. Because such feeding may also include puncturing ripe grapes to suck the juice, the bird is often unpopular. Pairs tending their fragile cup nest slung between twigs may be inconspicuous in their sober green and grey but, at times, large movements and migrations occur and birds may pass over in flocks with a constant chorus of peevish, thin, squeaky calls.

Some of the many honeyeaters, searching out nectar-bearing flowers, were bound to find that the parks and gardens offered feeding places. In addition to native and now widely grown eucalypts, banksias, bottlebrushes, grevillias, correas, kangaroo-paws, and similar trees, there are introduced exotics from flame-trees and kowhai to fuchsias, snapdragons, abutilons, hibiscus, and foxgloves, all of which may attract nectar feeders. No species appears to be tied to semi-natural areas of this type but many pass through.

The small Eastern and Western Spinebills, *Acanthorhynchus tenuirostris* and *A. superciliosus*, with breast, throat, and nape patterned in chestnut, black, and white, and with bright red-irised eyes, often visit gardens of the south-east and south-west. Their bills are very long, slender, and curved, and the birds have still longer tongues for probing deep, tubular flowers. They dart in quick flight, the wings making loud whirring sounds, and they will hover and probe for insects and spiders.

In the south-east, the Yellow-faced Honeyeater *Lichenostomus chrysops* is often a garden bird. Dull brownish, with a yellow face band bordered with black, it is best recognized by its cheerful *chik-up* call. Its song is a four-note descending whistle, and it is noisy in defence of its nesting territory. The nest is the usual cup suspended in a twig fork of a tree. As well as taking nectar, it will hunt insects in the leaves of bushes and trees.

The largest of the honeyeaters are also garden and orchard birds at times. On the mainland the Red Wattlebird *Anthochaera carunculata* occurs throughout southern Australia. It is a large, long-tailed bird with streaky brown plumage enlivened by a yellow belly, silvery cheek patches, and a pair of dangling red cheek wattles. In Tasmania its place is taken by the slightly larger but very similar Yellow Wattlebird *A. paradoxa*, which has yellow wattles. This is a noisy and suspicious bird which settles on high branches only to peer round cautiously before coming down to feed. As well as nectar, it takes soft fruits and stone fruits of various kinds. It also chases insects and probes crevices for them, including gutters, eaves, and window frames of houses. Its loud, throaty coughing and choking calls, sometimes written as *chok-a-lock* or *tobacco-box*, and harsh *yaak* notes advertise its presence.

Its shallow twig nest is built in a fork of a tree or large shrub, and is aggressively defended. After breeding, it tends to flock in areas where winter flowers grow and, until recent times, it was considered to be worth shooting and eating.

The provision of open water, not only from pools and dams, but in parkland or as storage reservoirs, has encouraged waterside birds and waterbirds to live in close proximity to humans. For example, there is the widespread Magpie-lark *Grallina cyanoleuca*; it is a black-and-white songbird resembling a Magpie but it is a little smaller than a Rock Dove. It is a bird of the waterside and, in general appearance, appears to be some kind of passerine plover, although now it is thought to be a monarch flycatcher that became terrestrial

Above: *The boldly pied Magpie Lark* Grallina cyanoleuca *finds both food and mud for its nest cup at the water's edge. The male, shown here, differs in face pattern from the female.*
Below: *The Black Duck* Anas superciliosa, *with its finely marked face and blue bill, is Australia's commonest dabbling duck.*

Right: *In some areas, the introduced Mallard* Anas platyrhynchos *competes with the Black Duck as a bird of parks and ponds.*

and large. It is a ground-feeding species with longish legs and walks like a pigeon with nodding head. The plump-breasted body is often carried horizontally, head raised on a fairly slender neck, with strong tapering bill. As it flaps along easily on its broad, rounded, black-tipped wings, with its broad-fanned, black-tipped, white tail, there is a passing resemblance to a bird of the Masked Plover or Banded Plover type.

The Magpie-lark has loud ringing calls, sometimes accompanied by ritualized postures. In territorial display, the male and female perch near each other, calling anti-phonally, a ringing *tee-pee* from one answered by a *pee-o-wit* from the other, each momentarily raising spread wings above its back as it calls.

This bird tends to feed along the open edges of water and, in wilder parts and more arid places, the provision of dams for watering stock has aided its survival and spread, but it happily moves to well-watered suburban lawns and the bare open places in suburbs, perching freely on buildings. The nest is a stout mud cup, bound together with stems and roots, and with a softer lining. It is plastered on to the top of a horizontal branch or wooden structure such as an outbuilding beam or a telephone line support.

Of birds of permanent water, the most widespread is the familiar Black Duck *Anas superciliosa*. Present on waters of almost any type, fresh or brackish, throughout Australia, it has learnt to look to people as possible providers of food in parks and similar places. The dark-mottled plumage is relieved by a black crown, pale face with black lines slanting across the eyes and cheeks, and a blue-grey bill. It has a showier rival in the introduced Mallard *Anas platyrhynchos* of the northern hemisphere. Although the female Mallard is streaky brown with an orange bill, the male has a greenish-yellow bill, dark green head, white neck ring and chestnut breast. It has been introduced to city parks and, although these are said to be separate species, it interbreeds freely with the Black Duck, producing confusing hybrids. In both species it is the female that has the familiar loud quack, the male's voice being a little hoarser and higher pitched. The nest, lined only with duck down, is tucked into any sheltered hollow near water, on or above ground.

A more unexpected inhabitant of the waters in some suburban parks is the Swamphen *Porphyrio porphyrio*. It is a big-bodied, duck-sized bird, with long red legs and large, long-toed feet. It is black, with bright glossy blue on its breast and underside, and has a stout triangular bill and forehead shield of bright scarlet. It walks with a deliberate stride, flipping up the short tail to show white undertail coverts. In wild places it is a shy bird, sneaking out at night to feed on plants, but sprinting back into the cover of dense reedbeds if disturbed. In parks it becomes tame, and is more likely to walk openly over sunlit turf watching hopefully for offers of bread.

The Swamphen can grip strongly with its feet, and can clamber up among tall reeds to peer over the tops. It can also hold an object between fore and hind toes and may be seen standing on one leg with some food held in a raised foot while it eats it parrot fashion. It has sudden loud *kyok* calls and raucous shrieks. It lives in family groups with helpers that assist in nest making and in the care of the fluffy black chicks; but groups defend territories and it is a quarrelsome and intolerant bird. The Swamphen occurs throughout most of Australia where swamps or permanent waters are present.

Another unexpected species is a small gull with red legs and feet. This is the Silver Gull *Larus novaehollandiae*. It is an inland, marsh-breeding bird as well as a sea gull. When not breeding it disperses in search of food. It has discovered urban rubbish dumps as rich feeding sites. It also likes areas of short grass where it can find worms and other small creatures, and also rest. It is a species successful enough to spend a lot of the day apparently just lazing.

The Silver Gull may be seen resting in parties and flocks on parks, sports grounds, and large lawns, quickly moving in if it sees food being thrown down, usually as a fluttering mob with a chorus of cackling and mewing calls. It has moved into city squares where office workers may feed it. Where tame it is reluctant to move far, and it is the gull that appears on the cricket outfield in many matches, glad to benefit, like many other birds, from human activities.

Below: *A swimming duck, such as this Mallard, will raise itself and flap its wings just as humans would stretch stiff arms.*
Top right: *Like the ducks, this stout-billed Swamphen* Porphyrio porphyrio *may learn to come for food scraps at park ponds.*
Bottom right: *Although they are marshland breeders, these Silver Gulls* Larus novaehollandiae *have also learned to use artificial sites where they can laze and hunt for food.*

3
Mangroves

For birds, mangroves represent a kind of wet, coastal or estuarine woodland, which is peculiar in that the woodland floor is flooded with salt water twice a day, and alternates between soft mud that is rich in small creatures, and seawater that has little to offer the birds. Mangroves grow on muddy shores, reaching their maximum growth on northern and north-eastern coasts, but elsewhere occurring in suitable conditions in bays and on the tidal edges of creeks and rivers. On the landward side, they may merge into Tea Tree or Saltbush, or into taller woodland growth, but, in Western Australia, extend intermittently along coasts where they stand up alone above the low scrub and grasses of the dry land.

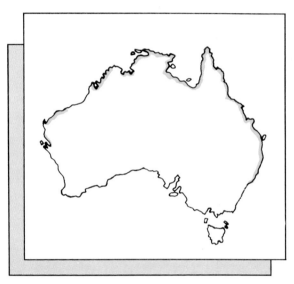

Mangroves have no serious competitors, because most plants cannot survive with roots submerged in salt water or salt mud. Mangroves overcome this in two ways. *Avicennia* or white mangroves, which tend to occur in shallower and more open sites and form a sparser growth, spread their roots near the surface mud and, from these, there spring up extensive mats of pencil-like aerial roots, standing up like some kind of sparse wooden lawn, covering the ground and tending to consolidate the mud. Except at high tide, they are mainly above water. Because they are adapted to shallower sites, these mangroves may occur towards the landward side of larger stands.

The denser mangroves of the north and east tend to be dominated by *Rhizophora* species in which some roots spring out well above mud level, arching in all directions to form a tangled thicket of woody roots spreading wide before plunging into the mud. They help to support the often large trees which rise to heights of about 15 metres (50 feet), and they provide surfaces to which intertidal shellfish and other shore creatures can cling.

At ground level, mangroves are home for a range of mud-dwelling creatures, including mudskipper fish and a multitude of small crabs. The damp, shady canopy of the trees shelters insects, including a large number of mosquitoes, while the trees provide nectar when in flower, and fleshy fruits at other times. For small birds, this is just another kind of woodland, and this can be best seen on the west coast. Here, woodland is confined to the south-western corner of Western Australia, tailing away to south of Shark Bay but, from the Bay northwards, stands of mangroves begin to appear, and the songbirds that haunt these are surprisingly close counterparts of some of those in the woodland further south.

Left: *The taller, denser mangrove growth consists largely of trees that produce arching roots above the mud surface; these are submerged at high tides but they allow the trees to take in oxygen at other times. These permit a woodland growth in shallow coastal seawater.*

The little Grey-breasted White-eye found among trees further south is replaced in the mangroves by the brighter Yellow White-eye *Zosterops lutea*; while the counterpart of the foliage-haunting Western Warbler is the Dusky Warbler *Gerygone tenebrosa*. The Grey-and-white Mangrove Robin *Peneoenanthe pulverulenta* replaces the White-breasted Robin found in south-western thickets. The Golden Whistler is replaced by the Mangrove Golden Whistler *Pachycephala melanura*, the two so similar that some regard them as subspecies of the same species; while the same fussily active Grey Fantail *Rhipidura fulignosa*, which occupies trees in the south, moves into mangroves as an acceptable substitute. Within the other mangroves of Australia there are also flycatchers, honeyeaters, and even a butcherbird which have their counterparts in woodland elsewhere.

Although the middle and upper layers of mangroves form woodland, the ground level offers something very different. It is a concealed coastal marsh with drier patches and a network of muddy drainage creeks, the larger ones creating openings in the mangroves. It provides a habitat for waterbirds that can tolerate the more enclosed conditions.

The Mangrove or Striated Heron *Butorides striatus* is a small bird which is about the same size as a magpie but looks larger. It has a well-feathered neck, a largish head with a stout dagger-like bill, and long, strong legs. Its blue-grey to greenish colouring makes it inconspicuous although, occasionally, rufous-brown individuals occur. The dark cap tapering back to a drooping point can be raised to form a shaggy crest in moments of excitement. The bird will stretch up its head when alert, but usually moves in a hunched posture with head held low. It clambers easily over or along mangrove roots, or over the mud. It flies on broad, rounded wings, tending to follow creeks, landing with raised head and ruffled crest. It hunts by watching and waiting, with a last-minute snatch; or it will slowly stalk its prey to approach closely enough. If necessary, it will plunge briefly into the water after food. (A small heron, believed to be the same species, occurs in North America where it has been observed deliberately floating small objects on the surface of the water near the shore to attract inquisitive fish which are then snapped up by the watching heron.) It is usually solitary and rather silent, but has harsh croaking calls that are more often heard from breeding birds. During the nesting season, its bill and legs become bright red for a while. The nest is a rather sketchy platform of stems on a branch or on low leafy vegetation, but usually over water. When perched in trees, it may use the bittern's trick when alarmed; stretching upright and becoming tall and thin, with bill pointing upwards; but the posture is less concealing than when used

by birds standing among reeds or rushes.

One other heron is an habitual haunter of mangroves. This is the Great-billed Heron *Ardea sumatrana*. Wide ranging from Burma to northern Australia but not common anywhere, it is found on the northern coasts from about Broad Sound in Queensland around to the Kimberleys. It is a great, heavy billed heron, brownish grey in colour with some paler streaking. It flies slowly and deliberately, and rarely gives voice to a deep guttural call. It is usually solitary, hunting the channels of mudflats and mangrove-bordered creeks. It roosts and breeds in mangroves and, being shy and intolerant of disturbance, prefers to make its big platform nest of sticks on a horizontal tree fork in areas of denser mangroves.

The Black Bittern *Dupetor flavicollis* is a little larger than the Mangrove Heron but is similar in build. Its blackish colour is relieved by a white throat and pale-streaked breast. It uses freshwater rivers and marshes but prefers to feed where creeks flow through shrubby areas and low woodland. On tidal waters, it finds these conditions in mangroves and extends its range into them.

Other herons and waterbirds make some use of mangroves. The coastal mudflats and beaches, and the mouths of rivers and creeks are good feeding grounds for birds. Some species that feed in such areas prefer trees when it comes to resting, roosting, or nesting. Stands of mangroves offer the obvious resting places on the borders of such feeding areas. In addition to being widespread inland, the White-faced Heron *Ardea novaehollandiae*, feeds on shores and reefs and occurs in the mangroves, as does the Pied Heron of northern

Left: *The Burdekin Duck* Tadorna radjah *is a mudflat-feeding specialist that finds mud and trees nest holes among mangroves.*

Below: *These White Mangroves grow in shallows on higher mud with more open growth, breathing through aerial roots.*

saltwater swamps. Both the Large Egret *Egretta alba* and its smaller, yellow-footed counterpart, the Little Egret *E. garzetta* also occur. These are usually colonial nesters, often in trees, and mangroves provide the kind of site required, near an abundant source of food, and over mud and tidal water that will help to deter predators. These birds build twig nests, fairly close together, and several species may occur at one colony. More waterbirds may join them in the mangroves for nesting.

The White Ibis *Threskiornis mollucca* with its bald, black head and black tips to rounded, white wings, and the slender, dark brown Glossy Ibis *Plegadis falcinellus* also occur in swampy coastal areas and will nest with other species, preferring the lower, bushier growth. Such colonies are often conspicuous, with visible untidy stick nests splashed with droppings. The adults, young birds, and squabbling neighbouring pairs are noisy, and there is often the smell of guano and decayed food remains although, in such situations, crabs and tides may help to keep the site clearer than those in still swamps or over dry land. Although the birds may be conspicuous, there is safety in numbers when predators are about, and isolation and inaccessibility make the successful rearing of young more likely.

Another coastal bird that may use the mangroves is the Pied Cormorant *Phalacrocorax varius*. One of the larger species, it is white below from face to vent, and black above from crown to tail. The bare face skin around the base of the bill is orange. It fishes mainly along the coastal shores, and nests in colonies, although it does not normally intermingle with other species. It uses a range of sites, including mangroves where these are available.

With the exception of the Burdekin Duck *Tadorna radjah*, which prefers to take its food from muddy surfaces, waterfowl make little use of the mangroves. It feeds on open mud at the water's edge, taking small creatures and plant material from the surface. It perches readily, and often rests in

Above: *The Darter* Anhinga melanogaster, *a thin-headed, snake-necked, fish-stabbing relative of cormorants, dries its wings on a mangrove perch after chasing fish underwater.*
Below: *The Little Egret* Egretta garzetta *feeds in shallow fresh or tidal waters and may rest and nest in mangroves.*

Above: *This small, hunched Mangrove Heron* Butorides striatus *is a skulking hunter largely confined to the mud and tangled roots of mangroves, nesting low in the vegetation.*

Below: *The scarce Chestnut Rail* Eulabeornis castaneoventris, *like the Mangrove Heron, is a marsh bird adapted to mangroves. It feeds on open mud and nests on raised sites.*
Bottom: *Like a blue flash, the Azure Kingfisher* Ceyx azurea *races and dives along the channels through the mangroves.*

trees. It is a species of the northern coasts extending also to similar coasts of New Guinea. With an all-white head, neck, and underside contrasting with a chestnut and black back, and wings that show the typical shelduck pattern of black, green, and white, it is a striking bird. The rounded white head with large, slightly upturned pink bill and the rather high-set pale-irised eyes, however, give it a slightly stupid expression; and, as it is a bird whose habits tend to protect it from predators, it lacks the speedy reactions needed to avoid modern human hunters armed with guns. It forms long-term pairs which maintain feeding territories but which also socialize with others. This can be a noisy affair because pairs show off by threatening the others with the loud rattling quack of the female backed by the hoarse, high whistle of the male. They have some problems with nesting sites, in that they need hollows in large, old tree trunks or on the surfaces of large branches, because all they can add is a lining of duck down. This tends to limit them to larger trees or to the type of woodland which tends to occur in more inland, swampy areas.

The other family of birds for which the muddy floor of the mangroves might have been expected to provide a desirable habitat is the rails. Although most are happy in muddy places, however, they need ground vegetation and herbage in which to hide, and this is in short supply in mangrove swamps. An apparently single exception is the rare Chestnut Rail *Eulabeornis castaneoventris*. About the size of a Swamphen, it is a big rail, with a slender, tapering bill. It is chestnut on the underside and olive-chestnut on the back; the head is grey with a whitish throat and offset by red-irised eyes and a greenish bill. It occurs in northern mangroves from the Kimberleys to the Gulf of Carpentaria, preferring areas of taller trees with thick leafy canopies. It usually occurs singly or in pairs, defending a breeding territory; it emerges from the mangroves at low tide to strut over the mud with upward-flicking tail, catching small crabs and similar creatures. When alarmed, it lowers its head and races for the cover of the mangroves, hardly ever flying. It is more often heard than seen, the calls including a cockatoo-like screech and deep drumming notes. The nest is a large stick structure built on mangrove roots or on the lower part of a sloping trunk, clear of tidal waters.

The other birds associated with water that make use of the mangroves are the kingfishers. In Australia *Halcyon chloris* is called the Mangrove Kingfisher. It is olive green on its crown, back, and rump, blue on its wings and tail, and white on its underside, throat, and around the neck. It ranges widely from Arabia to Australia but, although it occupies other wet habitats elsewhere, in Australia it is confined to mangroves. It is a heavy billed bird, similar to but distinctly larger than the Sacred Kingfisher *H. sancta*. It watches from a bare branch and swoops down on fish, crabs, and other small animals. It needs a cavity for nesting and may use a hollow tree, or drill a burrow into a tree termite's nest, a task in which both members of the pair co-operate.

The plunge-diving kingfishers, which have longer and more tapering bills and are more highly adapted to diving for fish, watch for their prey from perches in trees or bushes bordering or overhanging the water. The two Australian species use the edges of streams, rivers, and creeks. Where these waterways extend through mangroves or are bordered by mangroves in tidal areas, the kingfishers' ranges also extend through them.

The slightly larger Azure Kingfisher *Ceyx azurea* occurs along many waters in the north, and east of the Great Dividing Range; but the lovely Little Kingfisher *C. pusilla*, royal blue, with white on the underside, forehead and ear tuft, has a restricted range on the Arnhem Land and Cape York coasts and occurs more frequently in mangroves. Both have shrill, whistling call notes, and these, and the sight of a blue-rumped bird speeding along a creek low over the water is often all that one detects of them. At other times, they sit crouched on a perch until a fish is seen, when they swoop suddenly, plunging below the surface, and carrying the result of

Above: *The tiny, dagger-billed Little Kingfisher* Ceyx pusilla *finds small fish and shrimps in mangrove channels.*

Below: *The coast-haunting White-bellied Sea Eagle* Haliaeetus leucogaster *finds feeding perches and nest sites in mangroves.*

Above: *Like a small sea eagle, the mangrove-nesting Brahminy Kite* Haliastur indus *is mainly a scavenger of coasts and inlets.*

Below: *The Black Butcherbird* Cracticus quoyi *is a crow-like hunter of northern mangroves, with loud musical calls.*

Overleaf right: *The Grey Whistler* Pachycephala simplex *is the smallest and most flycatcher-like of the whistlers.*
Overleaf left: *From a conspicuous perch, the Mangrove Kingfisher* Halcyon chloris *plunge-dives for its prey of small fishes and shrimps.*

Above: *The rich-voiced male of the Mangrove Golden Whistler*
Pachycephala melanura *shares in caring for the young.*
Below left: *The plaintive-voiced Mangrove Warbler* Gerygone
levigaster *builds a pendant, pear-shaped nest.*
Below right: *The pendant, domed nest of the Large-billed*
Warbler G. magnirostris *looks like flood debris.*

Above right: *Similar to the Large-billed Warbler but greyer, the*
Dusky Warbler G. tenebrosa *has a neater, rounded nest.*

a successful foray back to the perch to eat it.

There are few large raptors in the mangroves. The coast-haunting White-bellied Sea Eagle *Haliaeetus leucogaster* and the fish-hunting Osprey *Pandion haliaetus* may sail over on shore patrols, or rest briefly on some high, dead branch, but they prefer more open places.

The bird at home in the mangroves is the Brahminy Kite *Haliastur indus*. It looks more like a small sea eagle than a kite. It is conspicuous for, although the young are greyish brown, the adults are chestnut-brown with blackish primary wing feathers, and the head and breast are white. The wings are blunt tipped and the tail is broad and slightly rounded at the end. In flight, the wingbeats are slow and deliberate, but the bird spends much of its time slowly soaring and gliding. It takes any creature small or weak enough to be caught, and also feeds on carrion, and stranded or dead fish. Although often solitary, it may also gather in numbers where food is plentiful. It is agile on the wing, and able to swoop down and snatch food from the surface of the sea with its feet. It may carry it to a perch or feed on the ground, but small items carried in the feet may be broken up and eaten while on the wing. It will snatch lizards or insects from the twigs and leaves of trees, and hunt low among the mangroves and over the creeks. Its food is mainly found by patrolling the tide's edge, however.

The Brahminy Kite has shrill weak whistling and mewing calls. Its nest of twigs and various debris is built well up in a tree. The female does most of the incubation of the eggs and care of the young birds while the male hunts and brings food; later both hunt to feed the growing young. It occurs throughout the mangrove region but also uses the barer, more open shores, and may penetrate inland for some distance along tree-lined watercourses.

There is another predator in the mangroves of Northern Territory and Queensland. This is the Black Butcherbird *Cracticus quoyi*, which is half as large again as other butcherbirds. It is black in colour except for a pale-blue base to the heavy, tapering, hook-tipped bill. In the eastern Queensland population, immatures and some adults have rufous plumage with some dark mottling. In spite of its size and strength, it is a shy species, usually glimpsed moving from tree to tree in level flight with rapid wingbeats, but, like many skulking birds, it is more likely to be identified by its voice. It compensates for inconspicuousness with loud, fluty, currawong-like calls and a song of three distinct notes, the middle one loudest. Its heavy bill enables it to catch and kill small birds, lizards, and similar creatures. It also takes nestlings and eggs as well as insects. It is probably encouraged to frequent mangroves because it is able to eat small crabs and other crustaceans. It will also eat fruit when available. This bird also ranges into rainforest and other thick forest nearby. The nest is a twig cup built high in a tree.

Within the foliage and branches of the mangroves, it is the smaller songbirds that predominate. When, in the Ice Age periods of the past the sea-level was lower and New Guinea was joined to Australia, the mangroves of the two lands probably joined in a continuous belt. Certainly, Australia and New Guinea do share species of birds and some may have moved south to Australia at this time while others, which seem not to reach further than Cape York may have made the relatively short crossing of the Torres Straits at a later date. Once in Australia, they have been isolated long enough to evolve distinct subspecies and species.

In some families, species have diversified so that they can co-exist even in limited mangrove zones. There is evidence of this in the Whistlers, warblers, and honeyeaters. On the northern coasts, the Grey Whistler *Pachycephala simplex*, a bird of forest, extends into the mangroves, using the upper leafy canopy. It is the smallest of the whistlers and is rather slender billed. On Cape York it is grey headed with a green back and some yellow on the underside. In Northern Territory, however, the Grey Whistler is buffish brown above and white below. It hunts insects among the leaves of the higher branches, where it also tends to place its small cup nest. The

The noisy and sociable Mangrove Honeyeater Meliphaga fasciogularis *searches for insects and nectar and is here seen visiting the blossoms of an* Erythrina *tree in a coastal town.*

calls and song are whistled notes of different pitches.

A more committed mangrove species is the Mangrove Golden Whistler *P. melanura*. Like its woodland counterpart, the male has a black head, white throat, green back, and yellow underside, but it has more black on its nape and throat band, and it is a little smaller with a thinner bill. His mate can be identified by her blackish tail and some yellow on the underside. They move steadily through trees searching for insects, and the male has a similar melodious song phrase to that of the Golden Whistler *P. pectoralis*, with the same abrupt ending. The nest is tucked into a tree fork.

The White-breasted Whistler *P. lanioides* is wholly adapted to the mangroves. Its bill is large and stout and, in feeding, it spends much of its time hopping over the mud and feeding on tiny crabs and other crustaceans with which the strong bill can cope. It will also take insects. It usually occurs on the seaward side of the mangroves and is a resident occupying a large territory. The male is grey above and white below; the black head is bordered behind with chestnut which extends in a broad band across the upper breast. The female is an undistinguished buffish-brown bird, with a streaky throat and breast, rather similar to a female Rufous Whistler *P. rufiventris* but larger. It has a long, loud, and strident song, as well as whistling call notes. Its nest is sited in thick mangrove growth, but is lower down than those of other species of whistlers.

Most mangroves have two overlapping warbler species. The Mangrove Warbler *Gerygone levigaster* occurs from the Kimberleys to New South Wales. It tends to prefer the shorter and bushier *Avicennia* mangroves growing on the landward side of the larger stands. It eats small insects, hunting among the trees from the ground upwards, peering, snatching, and at times hovering to pick off an insect. It is a small, inconspicuous, greyish-brown bird, whiter below and with a narrow, white eyebrow stripe. Its song is a clear, plaintive, rising and falling cadence like that of the Western Warbler, sung almost continuously when birds are nesting. The nest is a pear-shaped structure with a side entrance, built of strips of dry plant material and stems bound together with spiders' webs and suspended from the tip of a leafy twig.

The two other warblers that share its range, but replace each other, tend to prefer the taller, denser mangroves. The Large-billed Warbler *G. magnirostris* occurs from South Queensland to the eastern Kimberleys. It is a non-descript brown bird with a narrow white eye rim. It hunts insects as other warblers do. Soft, chattering notes are used between members of a pair, and the song is a series of rising or falling slurred notes uttered in an emphatic and jerky fashion. Externally, its domed nest is a very untidy structure and, when suspended from lower twigs, looks rather like the flood debris that is often lodged in creekside trees.

From the western Kimberleys to Shark Bay, this species is replaced by the Dusky Warbler *G. tenebrosa*, a paler greyish-brown bird with an indistinct whitish eyebrow stripe. Its calls and songs are similar to that of the Large-billed Fly-eater, but more subdued. It hunts insects at all levels in the mangroves. Its nest, pendent like those of the others, is more neatly rounded.

Honeyeaters also move into mangroves, but only two or three could be regarded as habitual mangrove species. One is the little Red-headed Honeyeater *Myzomela erythrocephala*; the male is black with scarlet head and rump while the female is mostly brown. It has a slender, curved bill and, in addition to feeding on insects, takes nectar from flowers, here supplied by the mangroves themselves and by parasitic mistletoe. These are restless, inquisitive birds, often associating sociably with other small birds such as warblers and white-eyes, or with other small honeyeaters. They tend to keep to the upper foliage of trees. They have shrill, squeaky calls and a short, harsh repetitive song phrase. The nest is a tiny cup of fibrous material suspended between forked horizontal twigs. This species occurs in northern mangroves from the Kimberleys to Cape York, and across the water in southern New Guinea.

The Mangrove Honeyeater *Meliphaga fasciogularis* is a larger and more typical honeyeater with a rather slender build. It occurs from New South Wales to the Queensland coast south of Cape York. It appears to be part of a double invasion from New Guinea; having originated from the New Guinea stock of the Varied Honeyeater *M. versicolor* and become a distinct form in isolation in Australia. The Varied Honeyeater has made a second invasion across the Torres Straits and is now present to the north of the Mangrove Honeyeater in the mangroves of eastern Cape York. The Mangrove Honeyeater is greyish brown with yellow edges to the flight feathers of its wings and tail. It has a grey crown, a black stripe through the eye, and a white neck patch. The throat is yellow barred with brown, the upper breast greyish brown, and the belly striated. The Varied Honeyeater is a little larger and browner, with yellowish throat and underside and with dark streaking on breast and belly. Active, noisy, and inquisitive birds with loud, varied, musical calls, they rove through the mangroves, often in small parties, examining foliage and blossoms for insects and nectar. The Varied Honeyeater has a loud, vigorous, mostly melodious

Above: *Like other mangrove species, the Varied Honeyeater* Meliphaga versicolor *will visit flowers of exotic planted trees of coastal towns, like this Erythrina, in search of nectar.*
Below: *The smaller, duller Rufous-banded Honeyeater* Conopophila albogularis *also feeds in nearby swamps and woodlands.*

Left: *The Northern Fantail* Rhipidura rufiventris, *more sluggish than others, hawks insects from a perch in flycatcher fashion.*

Right: *The Shining Flycatcher* Myiagra alecto, *here at its lichen-decorated nest, is an active, excitable insect hunter.*

call, while those of the Mangrove Honeyeater are less varied, but clear toned and more musical. Both will also explore coastal scrub, planted trees, and gardens and parks of human settlement along the coast; and the former ranges to the mangroves and trees of offshore islands. The nests are cup shaped and suspended by the rim from thin twigs, usually in forks. They may be built fairly low down, and those of the Mangrove Honeyeater are sometimes less than 1 metre (3¼ feet) above high-tide level.

At times, other northern honeyeaters range into the mangroves. One of the more regular visitors is the Rufous-banded Honeyeater *Conopophila albogularis* of coastal Northern Territory and western Cape York. Midway in size between the Red-headed and Mangrove Honeyeaters, it is brown with yellow wing and tail edges, a grey head, and white underside with a broad reddish breast band. It feeds on insects and various small invertebrates, and on nectar which it also gathers in nearby paperbark swamps and eucalypt woodlands. It may occur in loose flocks and may associate with other honeyeaters. It has twittering calls and a thin, squeaky song. The nest is a deep purse-shaped structure of bark fibres and grass stems, bound with spiders' webs. It is suspended from thin twigs or leaf stalks near the tip of a branch, usually partly concealed by overhanging leaves. Like the nest of the Mangrove Honeyeater, it is often low down very close to the high-tide level, suspended over water. Nest building and incubation seem to be the female's responsibility.

The other typical mangrove birds are mostly single representatives of families. The Yellow White-eye is a tiny yellowish-green bird with a white eye rim and a thin bill. Pairs or small flocks work their way through the upper foliage layers searching for insects and taking nectar from flowers. They will also range into nearby forest and scrub. Their passage is usually marked by a chorus of thin, high-pitched nasal notes, and breeding birds have a surprisingly loud, warbled song. The nest is a tiny deep cup of thin grass stems and spiders' webs, slung between thin twigs in a high horizontal fork. This species occurs in western and northern mangroves, but is absent in the east from Cape York southwards, where its place may at times be taken by the more widespread Grey-breasted White-eye.

The Grey Fantail is a woodland bird that also occurs in mangroves, working mostly through the upper foliage, switching its wide-fanned tail and darting after the insects it

Below: *Like its commoner Grey Fantail relative, the Rufous Fantail* R. rufifrons *pursues insects in jerky flight with spread tail. The small, neat nest is bound with spiders' webs.*

disturbs. In the north, from the Kimberleys to Cape York, the Northern Fantail *Rhipidura rufiventris* also occurs, and in both north and east the Rufous Fantail *R. rufifrons* may also be present. These tend to feed more sedately, the latter often hunting at lower levels, and the former tending to watch from a perch and flying out to catch insects in mid-air.

There are two monarch flycatchers for which mangrove is a primary habitat. One is the Shining Flycatcher *Myiagra alecto*. This has a strong bill, prominent-naped head, and a frequently fanned tail. The male is wholly black, glossed with blue-green, while the female has the head similarly coloured, but throat and underside white, and back, wings, and tail chestnut. Mainly insect eaters, they move through the mangroves in rapid, short flights and hops, tending to erect a slight crest and to spread and switch the tail when excited. They feed right down on to mangrove roots, swamp litter, and mud, and will also eat tiny crabs and molluscs. This species and the White-breasted Whistler would seem to be the only mangrove songbirds that actually get their feet muddy. The calls range from low guttural croaks to rasping notes and whistles, and there is a short piping song. The cup nest, set into a twig fork, is bound round the outside with fine spiders' webs and on these, are stuck flakes of bark and dead leaves that help to conceal it. Shining Flycatchers prefer the denser mangroves of the north but also range into paperbark swamp and waterside rainforest, as does the next species.

The more soberly coloured Broad-billed Flycatcher *M. ruficollis*, which resembles the females of Leaden and Satin Flycatchers, is a pale, glossy, blue-grey bird with pale chestnut-orange on throat and breast, and a white belly. The female resembles the male. The bill is a little broader than the bills of other monarch flycatchers, but it is flattened and looks thin in side view. This is a quieter bird than the last, in manner as well as in plumage, and spends more time on a perch sitting and looking before flying out after insects. It shows the tail-quivering that seems typical of some of these species. It has a two-syllable, whistled *too-whee* call. It builds a typical bark and lichen-coated nest.

Because robins are adapted to all the inland woods and scrub, it is not surprising to find one in mangroves. The Man-grove Robin is ashy grey on its back, darker around the eyes and on the wings and tail, and white below with a white patch on either side of the base of the tail. It moves and feeds quietly in the middle and lower levels of the mangroves, clinging to upright branches and tree trunks, and searching among mangrove roots and debris, as well as on drier ground. Like other mangrove birds, it will take tiny crustaceans as well as insects. The calls are a soft, mournful, double note, difficult to locate, and a small abrupt note; while the song is a varied musical whistling. Although this species is usually unobtrusive, breeding birds may display with fluttering wings and with tail spread to show the white patches. The nest is a small cup tucked in a mangrove fork.

Other species use the mangroves at times; one is the north-coast representative of the shrike-thrush group. The Rufous Shrike-thrush *Colluricincla megarhyncha* is a warm-brown, big-billed bird of moist coastal regions. It feeds down on to the ground in rainforest and well-wooded gullies; but keeps to the higher branches in mangroves.

There are many other species which casually visit mangroves; for them it appears as a tide-washed extension of the woodland and forest in which they more usually occur.

Below: *Although soft fruits are lacking, this Yellow White-eye* Zosterops lutea *is very similar in feeding and other habits to its dry-land counterpart, the Grey-breasted White-eye.*

Top right: *Like its woodland counterparts elsewhere, the quiet and unobtrusive Mangrove Robin* Eopsaltria pulverulenta *feeds low among the branches and roots of mangroves.*
Bottom right: *The Rufous Shrike-thrush* Colluricincla megarhyncha *frequently feeds among mangroves.*

4
Rainforests

Biologically, rainforest is the richest type of country in the world, but it needs reliable and plentiful rainfall. The continent of Australia, however, lies in a dry zone and lacks mountains. Even where wet winds occur, they tend to need the turbulence and air currents created by mountains before rain will fall. It is only the ridges of the Great Dividing Range, catching the persistent easterly winds, and the higher ground of the north-west which meets the monsoon rains from the north-west, that produce the high rainfall and allow a vigorous growth of vegetation. Rainforest occurs mainly on the eastern side of the range in Queensland, and occurs decreasingly and more sporadically in scattered localities as far south as Tasmania. In the north, from the Kimberleys to the Gulf of Carpentaria, there are small areas of monsoon forest or false rainforest in scattered limited areas on the coast or along rivers in the deeper gorges. In its long spread from south to north, Australian rainforest shows changes in its vegetation, and three types can be recognized although they merge into each other. Temperate rainforest occurs on mountain tops and on high ranges from Tasmania north, inland, to the New South Wales – Queensland border.

As with all rainforest, the trees are tall and close, forming a thick canopy layer of foliage that excludes much of the light and retains a moist atmosphere at lower layers. Shrub layers are reduced or absent, but the wetter atmosphere encourages the growth of epiphytic plants on the trees. In temperate rainforest, the dominant trees may be antarctic beeches or a native conifer. Ferns and tree ferns occur at ground level, and lichens and mosses grow on the trees, but there are few vines or lianas.

Subtropical rainforest occurs coastally in New South Wales north to the Richmond river, and inland on higher ground to near Cooktown. It has a wider range of tree species, including palms, usually with a thick canopy at 10 to 27 metres (33 to 88 feet), with a few tall trees protruding and a second shade-tolerant tree layer below. Ferns as well as moss grown on the trees, and there are vines and lianas.

In tropical rainforest from about the Richmond river to northern Cape York, there are many different species of trees which may be over 30 metres (100 feet) tall, and many of which produce fruit. They may form about three foliage layers. Palms, lawyer vines, and lianas are common. There is a little ground cover apart from ferns but many more epiphytes grow on the trees. Trees often have big, buttress-like root flanges. The monsoon forest of the north-west shares some of these characteristics but is poorer in the size

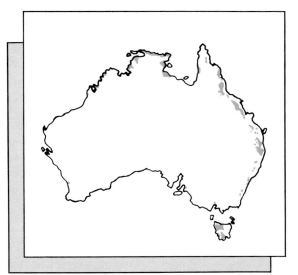

and variety of the vegetation, although it does support a small number of rainforest species.

In the wetter past, the Australian rainforests must have been continuous at times. Now they are isolated as separate tracts, made still smaller by tree felling. The birds in them have been isolated long enough in some instances to form subspecies or species of their own, but past links with New Guinea are obvious. In Australia, the number of species which rely mainly on rainforest for their existence increases dramatically from south to north, and over half are also present in New Guinea or nearby island groups.

Tropical rainforest is rich in birds, but they are not easy to see. Many fruits, flowers, and insects occur in the canopy layer, and birds feeding on them may spend much of their time hidden up there. Below, it is gloomier, and cluttered with tree trunks, saplings, and vines. In this poor light, many of the birds skulk and are inconspicuous, even if some make up for it by advertising their presence with loud songs and calls. Unlike the birds of harsher environments, which may need helpers for a single successful nesting, birds of areas such as rainforest, where there may be an abundant supply of fruits and other foods, are able to spend less time hunting for it. Females may be able to manage the nesting and the rearing of young alone and, in some species, males develop elaborate advertisement and courtship displays which take up much of their time during the breeding season.

The bowerbirds show stages in the evolution of bright plumages and of bower-building behaviour which bring bright-coloured males down to the forest floor. The females make cup-shaped twig nests in trees. The catbirds are the least specialized. Like all the bowerbirds, they feed mainly on fruit and insects. They are inconspicuously plumaged in glossy green with yellowish-streaked undersides, and they advertise themselves with loud, wailing *meow* calls. The Green Catbird *Ailuroedus crassirostris* of subtropical rain-forest, with its greyish-streaked head, is replaced in tropical rainforest by the Spotted Catbird *A. melanotis* which has a dark cheek patch and a lighter, buff-coloured face. They not only appear to lack display areas but help the females in nesting.

The Tooth-billed Catbird *A. dentirostris* of tropical rain-forest is a drabber, dull-olive colour with white-streaked underside. The male clears a patch of forest floor several metres across, however, strips off large leaves with its notched bill, and lays them on this area with the pale undersides upwards. Perched a little above the cleared space, he sings a loud song of weird whistling, spluttering, and hissing notes. When a female arrives, he displays on the area, fluffing feathers and twitching wings and tail; he then mates with her. It is a polygamous species and males take no part

Left: *Tall-trunked trees and an abundance of ferns flourish in the moist atmosphere of this temperate rainforest region of the mountain areas of eastern Australia.*

Above: *The loud, wailing* meow *calls draw attention to the otherwise camouflaged Spotted Catbird* Ailuroedus melanotis.

Below: *For the striking male of the Regent Bowerbird* Sericulus chrysocephalus, *the display plumage appears more important than the relatively small bower that it builds.*

in the nesting and rearing the young.

The male of the Regent Bowerbird *Sericulus chrysocephalus* is vividly coloured in black with big yellow wing patches, yellow on the top of head and nape, and with a reddish forehead and yellow-irised eyes. The female is dull brown. It inhabits subtropical rainforest, feeding mainly on fruit such as figs, but the bird will also raid orchards. Striking as the colours are when the bird is seen in the tree tops or in its direct, starling-like flight, it is even more conspicuous at ground level. The male builds a small bower, sometimes hidden among ferns and undergrowth of the forest floor. Two clumps of twigs 20 to 30 centimetres (8 to 12 inches) high are stuck into the ground to form parallel walls curving slightly inwards, the narrow avenue between them floored with fine stems. It may be decorated with a few scattered dead leaves, snail shells, seeds, or berries. Here the male makes subdued chatterings and grating noises, probably relying on his bright colours for advertisement. When a female joins him he moves jerkily, twisting his head to show off the bright colours, and crouches to display his spread wings and tail. The male may pair with several females, taking no part in the nestings.

The other bright bowerbird of the Australian rainforests is the Golden Bowerbird *Prionodura newtoniana*. It is a little smaller than other species. The female is olive brown in colour with a greyish underside, but the male has the whole underside and outer tail feathers coloured a shining, golden or orange-yellow. He has a small yellow patch on the crown of the head and a larger one on the nape, both of which can be fluffed up in display. In the higher parts of mountain rainforest in north-east Queensland, the male bird selects two bare saplings about 1 metre (3¼ feet) apart with a low perch bridging the gap. Collections of twigs are interwoven about the base of each sapling and, over a period of several years, these are built up into two conical masses up to 3 metres (10 feet) high, joined at the base, and with the low perch between them. They may be decorated with blue-green and green lichens, flowers, and sometimes berries – the objects are usually green or white in colour. Groups of males build their bowers quite close to one another. On its perch, the male

sings an unmusical collection of rattling, twanging, wheezing, and loud chattering notes. When a female approaches, the male jerks and bobs with his crest raised and tail fanned. In this species the male is again polygynous.

The other brightly ornamental songbirds, the birds of paradise, also occur and are almost restricted to rainforest. As there is among the bowerbirds, there is a duller, inconspicuous species. The Trumpet Manucode *Phonygammus keraudrenii* has purple-glossed, black plumage, a slight spiky crest, and red-irised eyes. The male has an odd deep call like a slowly creaking door. They stay high in the trees of tropical rainforest, feeding on fruit, such as figs. The male appears to help with the nesting, and the female has the strange habit of taking over new nests of other bird species, including those of birds of paradise, to use for nesting.

The other Australian birds of paradise are the riflebirds. There are three species which are very similar and closely related, possibly evolving from a double invasion from New Guinea. They are rather squat in build and have strong legs and short tails; the bills are quite long and are slightly curved. These birds often feed by clambering about on tree trunks and branches, probing under loose bark for insects but, at other times, they take fruit, climbing and clinging with equal agility. The females are brown or olive, with a pale eyestripe and underside, and fine dark breast bars. The males are black, with a large, triangular, glossy blue-green throat patch, and similar vivid colour on the crown and central tail feathers. The Paradise Riflebird *Ptiloris paradiseus*, of southern subtropical rainforest, has scalloped iridescent edges to its breast feathers. Victoria's Riflebird *P. victoriae*, of tropical rainforest, has a shorter bill, a small throat patch, and a mainly iridescent breast. Its tropical rainforest range overlaps that of the Magnificent Riflebird *P. magnificus*, also present in New Guinea, which is a little larger and longer billed, with a large, gold-bordered throat patch and purple-glossed breast.

All three species display in similar fashion, usually on

Above: *The soberly coloured females and young of the Paradise Riflebird* Ptiloris paradiseus *are more often seen than the resplendent treetop-displaying black and iridescent males.*

Below: *The Golden Bowerbird* Prionodura newtoniana *displays perched between two towers of twigs built around saplings.*

very high, exposed, horizontal branches. The male rears up, throws back his head and expands his throat patch laterally, and also cocks his tail. He fluffs out the belly feathers and spreads the wings fully, bringing them round as two fans until the tips touch in front of the body. The bill is open in calls that expose the lime-green mouth-lining, and the head turns from side to side, the bill appearing to stroke the wings. The first two species have a strident, long, two-syllable *yaas-yaas* call. The Magnificent Riflebird has an explosive whistled phrase - *weeoo, weeoo, chooweet, woo*; and deep growling notes but, in display, only odd blowing, swishing, and croaking noises occur, and the green mouth lining is not shown. Males in immature, female-like plumage also display in these species. A heavy rustling noise is produced, in flight and during displays, from the plumage. Females visit displaying males to mate, and nest on their own.

Some of the ground-living birds of rainforest are also striking in appearance and behaviour, even if they lack a vividly patterned plumage. The tropical rainforest of eastern Cape York harbours the Cassowary *Casuarius casuarius*, the rainforest counterpart of the dry-country Emu. About 2 metres (6½ feet) high, when standing upright, it has the typical bulky body with strong, long legs and comparatively slender head and neck. It walks over the forest floor, feeding mainly on fallen fruit, and will venture out into gardens or other cultivated areas for it. It is capable of a fast run when alarmed. The feathers are dense and coarse, looking like a thick coat of drooping hair. The plumage sheds rain and resists abrasion against vegetation. The legs are large and stout, with large claws used in fighting, but the wings are tiny, vestigial bunches of quills. There is a stout, bony

Below: *The Cassowary* Casuarius casuarius *is an unexpected giant of forest floors and clearings. It feeds on fallen fruit.*

Above: *The gaudy pattern of the bare skin of the Cassowary's head and neck changes with age. The bony casque may protect the head when the bird runs through undergrowth in panic.*

casque tapering to a ridge, perched on the forehead like a small helmet. It may help to protect the head when the bird crashes through forest undergrowth with head held low. The bare skin of the neck and head as well as the dangling neck wattles are coloured in vivid blue, purple, and orange. It is quiet, giving little warning of its presence other than a low rumbling, or a hiss of alarm, although quarrelling birds make louder roaring calls. As in the Emu, the female is larger, more brightly coloured, and dominant. The male incubates the large, green eggs in a shallow nest scrape and looks after the young. Although they are powerful birds, they are shy, and more likely to run than to argue, although they are unpredictable when with small young.

In the subtropical rainforest, one of the largest songbirds walks the forest floor. Albert's Lyrebird *Menura alberti* resembles the Superb Lyrebird of south-eastern forests, but has less exquisitely shaped outer tail feathers. It is a big bird with a longish neck, long, strong legs with big feet, and a long tail; it rather resembles a pheasant in size and shape. It is grey, with rufous on throat, back, and undertail coverts. It occurs in a limited area of south Queensland and northern New South Wales. It searches on the ground for insects and small creatures, digging and scratching with its feet, or demolishes rotten logs. It is a shy, furtive bird, skulking and

running, but it has a high-pitched, loud alarm shriek. Like bowerbirds, the male has a display ground, trampling down tangled vegetation, such as lawyer vines, to form a platform. On this, he displays to attract females, raising and spreading his tail in a great forward-tilted or vertical fan of filamentous feathers bordered by a stouter pair. It gives a loud, clear, continuous song, with intermittent, rattling calls and some imitations of other birds. The males are polygynous. The female builds a big domed nest, on the ground, or on a raised stump or in a rock outcrop. She lays only one egg, rearing the chick alone.

Other species have found that scratching the forest floor yields a good food supply. Two small songbirds, the Spinetailed Chowchilla *Orthonyx temminckii* of temperate rainforest and the Northern Chowchilla *O. spaldingi* of tropical rainforest, have become specialists at it. Generally thrushlike, they have very strong legs and feet. The tail feathers have strengthened shafts which project a little beyond the rest of the feather. They scratch the ground with alternate feet and, to dig more powerfully, the bird leans back, the strengthened tail resting with its tip on the ground and being used as a prop, while the bird makes long, raking scratches. The activities of these birds are visible as small cleared patches in the leaf litter and debris of the forest floor. Otherwise, they are unobtrusive inhabitants of the ground layers, flying little. The Spinetailed Chowchilla has a loud repetitive *hweet* call, and the Northern Chowchilla has a resonant *chow-chowchilla*. The former is brown above and white below; it is dark striped on the head and barred on the wings, with grey face and sides. The female has an orange throat. The latter species is dark brown with a black head, the female having an orange throat and upper breast. Their nests are large and domed, built on the ground or in fern clumps.

The small, brown, insect-eating Fern-wren *Crateroscelis*

Above: *The male Northern Chowchilla* Orthonyx spaldingi *shows its spiny tail at the entrance to its domed ground nest.* Below: *On its display perch, the male Albert's Lyrebird* Menura alberti *sings loudly and continually from under the shining canopy of overarching plumes of its spread and shivering tail.*

Above: *The white throat of the little Fern-wren* Crateroscelis gutteralis *stands out in the gloom of dark undergrowth.*

Below: *The clear, sweet song of the Yellow-throated Scrub-wren* Sericornis citreogularis *is more conspicuous than the bird as it slips through the lower storeys of forest vegetation.*

gutteralis and the scrub-wrens have parcelled out the various storeys of rainforest vegetation between them. The Fern-wren, with its white throat and eyebrow stripes, and black breast patch, skulks in the gullies and darker places of the forest floor in mountain rainforest between Cooktown and Townsville in northern Queensland; while the Atherton Scrub-wren *Sericornis keri*, which is dark brown with pale throat and belly, occurs in the lowest vegetation layer of that region.

The Yellow-throated Scrub-wren *S. citreogularis* of tropical rainforest in both the Cooktown region and in subtropical rainforest of New South Wales, overlaps both of these, feeding in the lower layers of vegetation. It is olive brown with a black face and yellowish-white throat and eyebrow stripes.

The Large-billed Scrub-wren *S. magnirostris*, is like the Atherton Scrub-wren but has a paler underside and light rufous-buff face. It occurs from mid Cape York to Victoria. This bird feeds in the middle layers of forest, taking insects from vines, lianas, saplings, and tree trunks and branches. The Tropical Scrub-wren *S. beccarii* replaces it in similar levels of tropical rainforest towards the tip of Cape York. It is more like a White-browed Scrub-wren in its white throat and marks above and below the eye, and in the white edges to some wing coverts, but it has red-irised eyes.

All these birds produce small, whistling and chattering notes and short, whistling or squeaky songs. The nests are domed, those of the first two at ground level, the others usually in a higher fork. The Large-billed Scrub-wren is exceptional in that it takes over old nests of other scrubwrens or warblers in which to nest.

Some forest-floor scratchers have used the habit to build

Above: *An excavator of the forest floor, a male scrub-fowl* Megapodius freycinet *stands on its great mound of leaf mould.*

Below: *Like the Scrub-fowl, the male of the Brush Turkey* Alectura lathami *scratches together a great mound of forest-floor litter to rot down and in which to incubate the buried eggs.*

incubators for their eggs. Two of the mound builders do this. One is the dark-brown and grey Scrub-fowl *Megapodius freycinet*. It is about the size of a domestic fowl, with a short tail, rather slender head and neck, but relatively massive orange legs and feet. The other species, the Brush Turkey *Alectura lathami*, is distinctly larger with a big, laterally flattened tail. The legs and feet are large, but less so than in the Scrub-fowl. It is glossy black, but its head and neck are bare, with fleshy hanging wattles at the base of the neck. Southern birds have red head and neck and yellow wattles but, in northern Cape York, the wattles are bluish white. The Brush Turkey occurs from Cape York to New South Wales in rainforest, and into thicker forest and overgrown creek margins to the west. It digs by grasping leaf litter as it scratches and then throwing it backwards. Working over an area of about 40 metres (130 feet) in diameter, it brings together leaf litter and some earth in a great heap which it tramples down, ending with a mound about 4 metres (13 feet) across and up to 1.5 metres (5 feet) high. This material rots while the bird tests the heat produced inside with its bill, and digs at it to adjust the temperature. The female is allowed to visit only for mating and egg laying. She scratches a hole in the mound, lays a large egg in it and covers it, the male completing the task. She may lay up to twenty-four eggs. They take about fifty days to incubate. At hatching, the downy chick digs its way to the surface and goes off alone – it is able to run and fly within a few hours.

The Scrub-fowl uses a similar technique. Although they are smaller birds, both members of the pair build a mound, scratching and throwing with their great feet, and several

Left: *The bright plumage and the slender tail of the White-tailed Kingfisher* Tanysiptera sylvia *make it a conspicuous object as it flies and hunts through the rainforest.*
Above: *A female Frilled Monarch* Arses telescophthalmus, *with the variable, intermittently present rusty breast colour very strongly defined, at its cup nest suspended between two supporting stems.*
Below: *A pair of Black-faced Monarchs* Monarcha melanopsis, *the male at the left, attend at the well-woven, drum-shaped nest.*

pairs may co-operate on the same mound which may be half as large again as that of the Brush Turkey. It is a mixture of earth and vegetable matter, with much more earth. The pairs tend the mound and both sexes help dig a tunnel up to 2 metres (6½ feet) deep in which the female lays a clutch, and then fills it in. As with the Brush Turkey, the downy chicks dig themselves out and scatter. Scrub-fowls occur in the Queensland rainforests and in the monsoon forests from Arnhem Land to the Kimberleys. Their range extends to forested creeks and swamps, and to the edges of mangroves and the shore. Both feed on the ground on fruits, seeds, and insects, but fly into trees to roost or when alarmed. The Brush Turkey has grunting and clucking calls, while the Scrub-fowl has a loud raucous crow and clucking calls.

Not all the species of the lower levels of rainforest are dull in colour. The White-tailed Kingfisher *Tanysiptera sylvia* is a summer visitor from New Guinea to lowland tropical rain-forest of Cape York. The central pair of its tail feathers are stiff and as long again as the bird itself. The whole underside is orange-buff, the crown and wings an iridescent blue, the face, nape, and shoulders are black, and the mid-back and rump are white, continuing to the slender white tail with shorter blue outer feathers. The stout bill and short legs are orange-red. The long tail appears to give it a level, floating flight, and it becomes conspicuous in more complex flutter-ing manoeuvres. The birds tend to use low, open perches, and swoop down for frogs, lizards, and insects on the ground or on tree branches or vines. The advertisement call is a repeated rising series of *choga* or *chop* notes, and there is a frequent high-pitched trill. The long tail is raised slowly when the bird lands, and may be swung slowly back and forth while it is perched. It prefers the more open lower levels of forest where termite nests are present. The nest is a hole bored into a termite mound about 50 centimetres (20 inches) high, the short tunnel and nest cavity having no lining. The cavity becomes fouled by food debris, bone castings, and droppings

Below: *With its big head and body and little tail, the Noisy Pitta* Pitta versicolor *bounds across the ground and seems designed for a terrestrial life, but roosts high in trees.*

Right: *The Pied Monarch* Arses Kaupi *is found in the forest and woodlands of northern Queensland. It is a member of a large family containing more than 130 species.*

of the young. The hatchlings are naked at first and the grow-ing feathers stay protected in the quill sheath until the birds are ready to leave the nest, giving nestlings an odd, spiky appearance.

The thrush-sized pittas of the rainforest floor should be its brightest ornament, but they tend to hide among under-growth and in dim, shady places. They have fairly large heads and large dark eyes; the legs and feet are well develop-ed, and the tail is small and short. They usually fly only for short distances, although one at least is partly migratory. The rounded wings show a sudden pattern of a white patch on black flight feathers when they are spread. The rump is pale blue above a very short, black tail. The birds bounce over the ground in long, springy hops, turning leaves and hunting insects, but also taking berries. Snails are eaten. They are rapped against a stone or hard object until the shell breaks. The sites where the birds deal with snails are re-used and can be identified by their little heaps of broken

snail shells. The sexes are similar and the domed nest is built and tended by both parent birds. The nest is usually raised above ground level among tree roots, on a stump, in a bamboo or fern clump, or in vines. The birds call with loud, whistling notes. They roost high in trees and may call from high perches in the morning or even during the night. Australia has three species.

The Noisy Pitta *Pitta versicolor* ranges through both tropical and subtropical rainforest. In winter, it moves from the south and some may winter in New Guinea. The head is black with two brown crown stripes. It has a bright-green back with sky-blue wing coverts, and a yellow-buff underside with scarlet lower belly and undertail coverts. It is better known by its call – a long two- or three-syllable whistle – than by its appearance. *Walk-to-work* is one rendering of it. There is also a loud *keow* call.

The Rainbow Pitta *P. iris* is very similar and probably evolved from a common ancestor. It occurs in monsoon forest of the north-west and is the only pitta species limited to Australia. It has the same green back and sky-blue wing coverts, but the black extends from head to underside, although the undertail coverts are scarlet. Its calls are similar to those of the Noisy Pitta. Its habitat preferences extend to bamboo thickets and to dense growth along watercourses. The nest sometimes lacks the concealing domed portion.

The Red-bellied Pitta *P. erythrogaster* occurs from the Philippines southwards, just reaching the Cape York rain-

Top left: *The White-faced Robin* Tregallasia leucops, *with its odd face pattern, feeds like yellow robins in open lower forest levels and is tamely inquisitive towards intruders.*
Bottom left: *The Grey-headed Robin* Poecilorhynchus albispecularis *is a quiet and inconspicuous inhabitant of the lower levels of forest. It has a monotonous, short, whistled song phrase.*
Below: *The seemingly bright plumage of the Purple-crowned Pigeon* Ptilinopus superbus, *here sitting on its sketchy nest, may be less conspicuous in fruiting trees.*

forests, from which it migrates to New Guinea in the dry winter period. It has a dull-green back, and a blackish head with rufous nape and blue ear coverts. The throat is black and the upper breast pale blue with a narrow black border separating it from a scarlet lower breast and belly. Its range overlaps that of the northernmost Noisy Pittas, and it extends into nearby forests and the thick undergrowth of rocky places. It has a quieter, mournful four-note whistle.

The middle storey of the forest, where vines, lianas, branches, and foliage provide insects and other small creatures, is the region of the flycatchers and robins, especially the black-and-white and grey-and-buff monarchs. There are two monarch flycatchers in which the top and sides of the head, mantle, wings, and tail are black. The underside and rump are white, and a broad white band across the back of the head and neck is fluffed up in moments of excitement. There is a bright-blue wattle around the eye. The male Pied Monarch *Arses kaupi*, of the southern Cape York rainforest, differs from the Frilled Monarch *A. telescophthalmus* of the northern Cape York rainforest in having a black band across the breast. The female of the former has a white spot in front of the eye, and lacks the wattle; while, in the latter, the female has a broad black breast-band and the sides of the neck are black. They feed by spiralling up branches in tree-creeper fashion and then fluttering out to catch the insects that they disturb. The calls are soft whistles, but groups of birds may chase one another, fluffing frills and feathers, in noisy chattering displays. In sexual display, the male ruffles its feathers and makes a buzzing, insect-like song. The nest is a hanging cup, slung between vines or twigs, of plant material bound with spiders' webs.

The Black-faced Monarch *Monarcha melanopsis* is a lovely pale blue-grey colour on its head, upper breast, and back, and rufous-buff on the underside; the front of the face and throat are black in adults. It inhabits rainforest and wet eucalypt forest right down the east coast, replaced as a breeding bird at the Cape York tip by the Black-winged

Monarch *M.frater*, which is similar but has black wings and tail. It hunts in creepers, branches, and leaves for insects, usually in pairs, and it is not particularly conspicuous except for a loud, rich whistling call of *why-you-which-you* or variations on it. The nest is a firm, neat cup of moss and bark flakes built into a twig fork of a tree or sapling. The southern population is migratory and some go to New Guinea in winter.

The Spectacled Monarch *M. trivirgatus* is rather similar to the last in appearance and range, but it is a bird of mountain forest rather than lowland. It is a deep blue-grey above with black face and throat, and has an orange-rufous breast with a band extending to the bill on either side. The belly and tail tip are white. Its hunting behaviour is more conspicuous than that of the last species, with frequent erratic fluttering and dodging, and fussy chattering and scolding calls when it is active. It also has clearer whistling notes and a short warbling song. The nest is a deeper and more tapering cup in an upright fork, bound with spiders' webs on which are stuck green moss and white spiders' egg cases. As with other

Right: *The raising of the shaggy crest, and the varying intensity of red in the bare cheeks indicate the changing moods of the Palm Cockatoo* Probisciger aterrimus. *The lethal-looking bill can manipulate small seeds as well as woody nuts and cones.*

Below: *The noisy sociable Shining Starlings* Aplonis metallica *are forest fruit eaters. This bird perches above one of the bulky domed nests in a tree colony where display occurs.*

monarch species, the female incubates the eggs but the male helps to feed the young.

There are three robins to be found in the mid-forest level; the White-faced Robin *Tregallasia leucops* in northern Cape York, the Pale Yellow Robin *T. capito* in southern Cape York and in temperate rainforest, and the Grey-headed Robin *Poecilodryas albispecularis* which shares the southern Cape York forests. The first and last feed in typical robin fashion, clinging to vertical branches and tree trunks, and occasionally dropping to the ground to catch an insect or spider, but the Pale Yellow Robin hawks insects in a more flycatcher-like way. All make cup nests which are tucked into forks of vines or saplings, and ornamented on the outside with moss and lichens.

The Pale Yellow Robin is yellow on the underside, olive on the back and head, and has a whitish face. The White-faced Robin is similar but brighter, with a bold white patch on the front of the face extending as a white line around the eye, and the rest of the head is blackish. The Grey-headed Robin is in muted shades, grey on its head and back, with a blackish band from the bill to a brown ear patch, and with white on the throat and around the eye. The back and tail are brown, the rump chestnut, and the wings blackish with white wing bar and tips. Their voices are similar, the first two having rather mournful single whistles, and the last having softer, single or double notes.

A brightly coloured fruit pigeon also uses these middle layers of the forest. This is the Purple-crowned Pigeon *Ptilinopus superbus* of the north Queensland tropical rainforest. It takes a large range of smaller fruits, particularly those of the laurels, and will range into other woodland when fruit-bearing trees are present. It is a small pigeon, not much larger than a shrike-thrush. The male is green on the upperparts with dark wing spottings, the crown is magenta-purple, the face green, the throat ashy, and there is a broad, bright-rufous band on the hind neck. The breast is blue-grey with a black lower border, and the flanks are green and white. The female is green with grey throat and a small blue crown patch. The bird flies among the trees, builds a twig platform nest, often in a vine tangle, and lays a single egg. The voice is a low, two-syllable *coo*.

This middle storey of the rainforest has its less conspicuous birds. Bower's Shrike-thrush *Colluricincla boweri* of the mountain rainforest of the Cooktown-Townsville region is

Right: Like some other birds of tropical forests, these tiny Double-eyed Fig Parrots Opopsitta diophthalma *feed on the flesh and seeds of figs.*
Below: The Double-eyed Fig Parrots feed in small, quiet groups. This is the subspecies of the Cape York rainforests, the male is on the left.

Above: *A Wompoo Pigeon* Ptilinopus magnificus *feeds its chick in the shallow twig nest; it takes the little bill in its own.*

Left: *Exceptionally among parrots, the Eclectus Parrot* Eclectus roratus *has, to human eyes at least, a female, on the left, more vividly coloured than her plain green mate.*

chiefly recognized by its song which consists of four quiet, rapid notes followed by three deep, plangent ones that carry for some distance. The bird itself is a dull dark brown in colour, paler on the breast with dark streakings, and has a large, stout bill. It forages in leaves, vines, and branches, swooping from one perch to another. The cup nest is set in a fork or vine tangle.

The upper part of the forest has the brighter array of birds. One black-and-white monarch, the White-eared Monarch *Monarcha leucotis*, feeds and nests high. It has white edges to its black wings and tail and four white patches on a black face, giving it a chequered appearance. A bird of tropical and temperate rainforest, nevertheless, it is rarely seen.

The Shining Starlings *Aplonis metallica* of the Cape York rainforest feed on fruiting figs and similar trees in flocks, sometimes in hundreds, in noisy, wheezing, and chattering masses. It is glossy green with a purple-glossed head, and prominent, scarlet-irised eyes. They nest communally in tall trees which stand alone or above the others. The bulky nests, woven from dry plant fibres, are suspended from twigs, sometimes close together and festooning the tree heavily. The nest is rounded with an entrance in the side, sometimes projecting as a spout. The young are drab brownish above and pale below. These birds fly fast and directly, and will fly through trees as well as over them. They also raid orchards, and visit mangroves and offshore islands.

The upper levels are also used by parrots. The largest, the Palm Cockatoo *Probisciger aterrimus*, is black with a big spiky crest, and a patch of scarlet skin across the cheek below the eye. Using its massive bill, it feeds on seeds, nuts, and other parts of plants, and it also takes some wood-boring insect larvae. It keeps mainly to the upper branches of high trees where rainforest meets woodland, but will still come down low for fallen seeding fruits. It is particularly fond of Pandanus Palm seeds. Its principal call is a deep *hweet-kweet* whistle, but it also has screeching and wailing calls. It

Above: *Rainforest honeyeaters are few. The streaky plumaged Macleay's Honeyeater* Xanthotis macleayana *feeds largely on insects that it finds among twigs, vines, and leaf tangles.*

Right: *Small, active, and aggressive, the Dusky Honeyeater* Myzomela obscura *ranges widely in search of nectar-rich flowers and will visit drier forest areas and local gardens.*

nests, and rears its single young, in a big tree hollow. In Australia, it is confined to northern Cape York.

At the other extreme, the tiny Double-eyed Fig Parrot *Opopsitta diophthalma* also occurs in isolated tracts of tropical rainforest in northern and south Cape York, as well as southern Queensland to northern New South Wales. Its 'double' eyes are actually dark markings shown by some foreign subspecies. It feeds mainly on the seeds of wild figs, usually in quiet and inconspicuous small groups, and makes small, squeaky calls. It has a fast and direct flight. It tunnels its own nest hole in a rotten branch. The three Australian populations differ in the pattern of blue and red patches on the forehead and face. Otherwise, the bird is green with blue flight feathers, a red mark on the inner wing, and yellow sides to the breast.

An oddity is the large, square-tailed and round-headed Eclectus Parrot *Eclectus roratus*, in which the male is less conspicuous than the female. She is dazzling in scarlet with a bright-blue belly, flight feathers, and collar, and a black bill. The male is plain green with blue flight feathers and scarlet underwings when it flies; his bill has a yellowish upper mandible. They are sociable, noisy birds with raucous

screeching cries. The tree-hole nest holds two young, and additional individuals appear to help feed them. In Australia, this bird occurs only in a part of Cape York.

There are two species of fruit pigeons which frequent the upper rainforest. The big Wompoo Pigeon *Ptilinopus magnificus* is green with a grey head, bright-purple throat and breast, and yellow on the belly, coverts, and undersides of the wings. It occurs in tropical and subtropical rainforest. It has a loud, deep *wollack-a-woo* call, and shorter notes. It is inconspicuous when feeding among foliage but, like some parrots, its presence is revealed by a rain of falling fruit. It builds the usual flimsy nest in which one egg is laid.

The smaller Red-crowned Pigeon *P. regina* has a plum-red forehead bordered with yellow, grey head, neck, and breast, and a green breastband and orange-yellow belly. It ranges throughout all rainforest and monsoon forest, and sometimes into other forest and mangroves. It feeds more in tall trees than the Purple-crowned Pigeon does. Its call is a run of accelerating coos. Its nest is often in a vine-tangle, sometimes fairly low down. When not nesting, the bird seems to be nomadic.

The Topknot Pigeon *Lopholaimus antarcticus* is confined

to eastern rainforests. It is so arboreal that it rarely settles on the ground. Like the fruit pigeons, it is acrobatic in pursuit of food, clinging and flapping among thin twigs. It is dark grey above, pale grey below, with two black bands across the tail. It has a stout red bill, a slightly lop-sided crest ridge on the forehead, and an odd, twisted brown ridge of crest feathers flopping back on the nape. It is relatively silent, with a short sharp note, and an occasional low coo. It is nomadic and was present in large numbers in the past.

Only a few honeyeaters are confined to rainforest. They tend to be drab in colour. Macleay's Honeyeater *Xanthotis macleayana* is found in the Cooktown-Townsville lowland forest. A dull-brownish bird with pale streakings, black cap, bare face skin, and greyish ear coverts, it clambers on branches, among dead leaf clusters and vine tangles, and eats mainly insects. It has a five-note *to-wit, too-weee-twit* call. Its nest is a deep cup of plant material and spiders' webs, slung in a twig fork.

The Green-backed Honeyeater *Glycichaera fallax* seems to feed entirely on insects. It is small and warbler-like, greenish above and yellowish below, and with thin, twittering, and squeaky calls. It feeds among the treetops on northern Cape York.

The Dusky Honeyeater *Myzomela obscura* is also small. It is dull brown with a slender, curved bill but, in its behaviour, it is a more typical honeyeater. Occurring in Queensland and northern rainforest and other forest habitats, it ranges in search of nectar-bearing flowers and insects. It is active, acrobatic, and aggressive; it gives voice to small, squeaky calls and a *tip-tip-eee-chip* song phrase. It builds a typical suspended cup nest.

In its entirety, the layered plant life of the rainforest encourages a complex, stratified range of species, some of which overflow into, and make use of, the other vegetative zones that border it, while others rely on the richness of the rainforest alone.

5
Eucalypt and Acacia Forests

The tall trees of Australian forests grade into the wetter rainforests and into the drier and more open woodlands. The forests are composed mainly of trees in which the height of the trunk is as tall, or taller, than that of the foliage canopy that it supports. Tall, straight, bare tree trunks are typical of these forests; and they contain some of Australia's finest scenery in places where massive-trunked trees rise sheer and smooth out of low shrubs and grasses, with the great heads of foliage carried high above. For birds, this tends to split the habitat, with a choice between the flowers and insects high above, or the low shrubby growth beneath, with little but space and bark between.

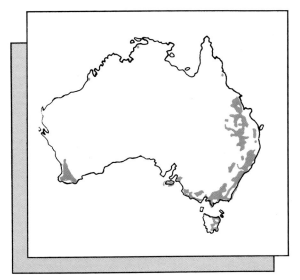

The dominant trees have tough, evergreen leaves and, for this reason, such forests are often referred to as 'sclerophyll forest'. The trees involved are usually eucalypts but, in one region, Brigalow Acacia is the dominant tree. There is some difference in the type of vegetation between wetter and drier areas, and eucalypt areas are usually divided into 'wet' and 'dry' forest.

Wet eucalypt forest is usually dominated in any one area by only a few tree species, sometimes by just one. Mature trees are mostly more than 100 metres (330 feet) tall, and in some areas up to 200 metres (660 feet). They usually form a closed canopy of foliage, with a thick shrub layer at lower levels. In wetter places, tree ferns grow. Towards the drier edges of forests of this type, the canopy is more open, and shrubs may be replaced by grasses. Such forest occurs in wetter areas throughout the forest zone, especially in New South Wales and in higher parts of the south-east. The big, dominant eucalypts include the giant Mountain Ash, Blackbutt, Sydney Blue Gum, Flooded Gum, and Karri.

Dry eucalypt forest occurs on less fertile soils. It usually has several codominant tree species and the mature trees are usually less than 100 metres (330 feet) tall. The canopy is more often broken than closed. The shrub layer has more tougher-leaved species adapted to drier conditions. Dominant eucalypts include stringy-barks in the east and Jarrah in the south-west. This type of forest extends intermittently down eastern Australia from about Mackay in Queensland to Tasmania and southern south Australia, with a small area in the extreme south-west.

Brigalow forest occupies an area of inland eastern Queensland, within the ranges of the Divide and extending to the western side of them, and into northern New South Wales. It has a patchy distribution. Brigalow is the dominant tree, often about 10 metres (33 feet) high, sometimes up

to 24 metres (80 feet). It may be dense, with a shrub layer and a herb layer, or more open with mainly herbs and grasses. There is a greater admixture of other tree species. These forests dominate the higher ridges of the south-east. They offer a good breeding refuge for a number of species that, having bred, prefer to move down to lower levels and coastal regions where food may be more abundant in winter. Some migrate north. A range of species is involved in a small-scale altitudinal migration comparable in some respects to those occurring in high mountain areas elsewhere in the world.

Gang-gang Cockatoos *Callocephalon fimbriatum* breed in holes high in eucalypts in forests in the south-east. This is a smallish, squatly built cockatoo with a short, stout bill, broad, rounded wings, and square tail. Either sex has a small, wispy, upcurved crest at the back of the head, and the male has a bright-red head and crest. Otherwise the plumage is grey, with a narrow, whitish margin to the feathers, and tinted yellowish or orange on the underside. They fly with steady, deep wingbeats and give a rasping, creaking growl with an upward inflection. In lowland, they seek out berry- and seed-bearing trees and shrubs, feeding silently except for occasional low growls and the patter of falling debris. They strip abundant food sources, spending most of the time among branches and often seeming quite tame. They take exotic fruits, such as hawthorns, firethorn, and cones of cypress conifers. They visit parks and suburbs.

The King Parrot *Alisterus scapularis* is another bird better known in its winter quarters. The male is bright red on his head and underwings, and has a yellow-irised eye. The back and wings are green, and the rump, tail, and nape are blue. On females and young, dull green extends to the head and breast. This parrot breeds in hollow eucalypts, the nest often well down in a hollow trunk. The tail is long. The flight is strong and easy, but with erratic twists and turns that aid it when flying among trees. The flight call is a high, harsh, double *crassak* or *chak*, and the male has a ringing whistle. It takes nectar, flowers, buds, seeds, and fruit, feeding for much of the time among the outer branches of trees; but, in winter, it often comes to the ground for food. It will visit orchards for fruit, and farmland to feed on maize cobs and potatoes, making itself unpopular. It is a noisy and rather wary bird, rising and flying to cover when disturbed.

Forest robins often move out in winter. Two similar species occur in the south-east, breeding in the shadier shrub layers of wet forest or fern gullies. The smaller Rose Robin *Petroica rosea* occurs from South Victoria to southern Queensland along the Great Dividing Range. The male is dark grey with a small, white forehead spot, rose-pink breast, and white belly. The female is brown with two buff

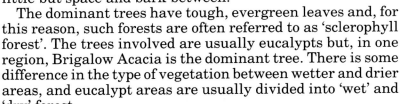

Left: *In forests, the trunks of trees are taller than the foliage mass they carry. Here, in the south-west, the huge trunks of Karri trees separate the foliage from the ground vegetation.*

wing bars, and grey on the underside. The Pink Robin *P. rodinogaster* of Tasmania and south Victoria is larger. The male is dark grey with a light magenta-pink breast and belly, and the female is similar to a Rose Robin but with a pale-brown underside.

They feed like flycatchers, perching with slightly drooped wingtips and upward-tilted tail, nervously flicking wings

Above: *This creaky voiced male Gang-gang Cockatoo* Callocephalon fimbriatum *gorging on berries of the introduced hawthorn moves from mountains to lower levels in winter.*

Below: *The King Parrot* Alisterus scapularis *is another species better known for its winter visits to orchards and farmland.*

and tail, and flitting off to snatch insects from twigs, or dropping to the ground for them. In both species, the nests are neat, rounded cups of moss and fibre, covered with a heavy ornamentation of lichens. They are fitted tightly into or on to open twig forks and are inconspicuous. The incubating female is fed by her mate; and both adults tend the young.

The Rose Robin has a low, throbbing, musical trill as a song, and a sharp, ticking call. The Pink Robin has similar ticking notes, but the song is subdued, sounding like a single, low, vibrant whistle which seems to be much further away than it really is. Both move, sometimes in family parties, to lower ground and more open areas in winter. They are quiet and retiring, but relatively tame and slightly inquisitive. In forest habitats, the Pink Robin feeds lower and at ground level, but in winter both may venture into open places, when the male's breast colour is bright and conspicuous.

The Yellow-faced Honeyeater has already been mentioned as a migrant species that, on passage, commonly occurs around human settlement; but, as a breeding bird, it occurs in wet eucalypt forests and in the thicker parts of dry eucalypt forests from Spencer Gulf round the south-east to northern Queensland. Its cup nest is suspended from twigs in the lower shrub layers. It defends a nesting territory, aggressively and noisily. Its breeding season song is a slow, descending, four-note phrase.

Another forest honeyeater, the Crescent Honeyeater *Phylidonyris pyrrhoptera*, shows local movements in at least part of its range. In southern Victoria it is a bird of lowland wet forests and extends into thick vegetation bordering creeks and streams; in Tasmania, however, it nests in alpine forest and then moves to coastal heaths with their greater abundance of flowering shrubs. The male is a slender, grey honeyeater with yellow edges to the flight feathers of wings and tail. It has a small white streak behind the eye, and is mainly white on the underside with a black crescent on

Above left: *The male of the small Rose Robin* Petroica rosea *helps feed the young in the neat, lichen-decorated nest.*
Top right: *The Crescent Honeyeater* Phylidonyris pyrrhoptera *is a nectar-hunting forest species known for its* egypt *call.*
Above right: *Noisily active, the Satin Flycatcher* Myiagra cyanoleuca *hawks after insects from bare perches among foliage.*
Left: *The crow-like Pied Currawong* Strepera graculina *is a wanderer in winter when it often occurs around towns, but nests in the tall trees of upland forest.*

either side of its breast; it has ashy grey flanks. The female is browner where the male is grey. It has a distinctive loud *e-gypt* or *ee-jik* call, accentuated on the second syllable, and providing one of its popular names. In winter, a short *jik* call is used. It is a bird of middle forest layers, and is more likely to be heard than seen. It usually occurs in small parties, feeding on nectar, insects, and sweet sap which oozes from trees. Its cup nest, bulkier than those of many honeyeaters, is built fairly low in a thick shrub or fern.

The Satin Flycatcher *Myiagra cyanoleuca* is another migrant songbird of forests. It catches flies actively and energetically among the treetops, watching from a bare twig and swooping out after insects that are usually caught on the wing. It often erects the small, peaky crest on the head, and swings the body and tail from side to side, quivering the tail vigorously. It calls noisily and frequently with rattling, wheezing, or buzzing noises, and the song consists of various, rapidly repeated, two syllable whistles. The male is glossy blue-black in colour with a sharply defined white lower breast and belly, and undertail coverts. The female is duller and her throat and upper breast are a warm, light orange-buff. These birds prefer the more thickly vegetated forest. The nest, which is often high up and out on the end of a dead branch, is a neat shallow cup of plant fibres, bound and matted with spiders' webs, and sparsely decorated with lichens. The webs bind it on top of a horizontal branch or into a bare fork. Male and female birds share nesting duties. After breeding, birds from the southern part of the range move northwards to New Guinea and its islands, but the north Queensland birds may remain. During migration, it occurs in more open lowland areas.

In the east, the Pied Currawong *Strepera graculina* has invaded, and scavenges around suburbs and farmland in social groups in winter to an extent that almost makes it a city bird. Its normal breeding grounds, however, are in the higher forest ranges where it breeds in scattered pairs. It is crow-like, but with a more rangy appearance, and has longer wings and tail, and a narrow, flattish-crowned head with very stout, dagger-bill and sharp, yellow-irised eyes. It has the slightly furtive but alert air of a bird about to commit a crime. It is black with white on the tail tip, base, and under-tail coverts; there is a white patch on the wings which is conspicuous when it flies. It occurs from Cape York to Victoria, and in Tasmania is replaced by the Black Currawong *S. fuliginosa* which lacks the white at the tail base and has a small wing patch. The latter has a more musical *karweek, weekkar* call and metallic conversational notes. Like the mainland bird, it breeds in mountain forest where its ringing call is a noticeable feature, and moves to the more temperate climate of the lowlands in winter.

Pied Currawongs have loud, ringing calls which tend to vary locally. They have odd throaty tones; a gutteral, wailing *currar-awok-awok-currar* or double *jabawok* seems to have given it the popular name, and there is a high *crik-crik* followed by a descending wail, and a rising and falling wolf-whistle. It has a distinctive, long-winged flight, casually easy with swoops and flaps. It feeds on small creatures, carrion, berries, and fruit, found on the ground and in the larger branches of trees. The nest is a cup of sticks with a finer lining situated in the fork of a eucalypt.

The Pied Currawong is the host of Australia's largest parasitic cuckoo. As large as a currawong, the Channel-billed Cuckoo *Scythrops novaehollandiae* needs large host species to rear its young, so it lays its eggs in the nests of crows and crow-like birds. It prefers tall forest, keeping to the upper parts of tall trees where it can find wild figs or similar fruits, and where it also finds currawong nests. Its great, long, stout, fruit-eating bill invites comparison with the toucans and hornbills of tropical regions. It has short legs, but the wings are long and tapering, and the tail long.

In flight it has the unmistakable cross-like silhouette. The call is a series of raucous *awk* notes, given from a perch or in flight. The bird is grey with dark tips to the wing feathers, and there is a broad dark bar and white tip to the tail. Like all cuckoos, it is disliked and mobbed by other birds. This species, too, is a migrant from the forests, wintering in New Guinea.

In addition to the currawongs, the forest regions have a true crow. The Forest Raven *Corvus tasmanicus* is as big as the Australian Raven *C. coronoides* but lacks the shaggy throat feathers. Its main distribution is in Tasmania where it is the only crow and can exploit the various habitats and opportunities. Elsewhere it is limited to a few scattered, south-eastern localities where it is the only crow that readily lives in forest regions under the closed canopy. It appears to rely on forest for survival, where it is a typical scavenger and opportunist, building its large stick nest high in a tree. Its call is a deep *korr-korr-korr-korror*, the last note tending to be prolonged into a long-drawn dying fall like that of the Australian Raven.

Left: *Largest and strongest of the Australian owls, the Powerful Owl* Ninox strenua *is a night hunter of the larger tree-living mammals and birds. Its strength has not made it bold, and it is a retiring forest bird living in scattered pairs.*

Above: *A great grotesque cuckoo with an oversized bill, the Channel-billed Cuckoo* Scythrops novaehollandiae *lays its eggs mainly in the nests of crows and crow-like birds.*

The forests have few large birds, but they are home to the biggest owl. The Powerful Owl is like a huge Boobook Owl, and has the same large, staring eyes with orange-yellow irises. Its plumage is brown and barred, and the bird is up to about 65 centimetres (25½ inches) tall. It lives in pairs, holding permanent territories. They roost by day, near each other on the branches of high forest trees. The call is a loud, slow rather mournful *woo-hoo*. In hunting, it takes mainly tree-living mammals such as possums, and will also take the larger perching birds. It nests in a large hollow tree, the female incubating the two eggs alone. In spite of its size and

Below: *The Australian Raven* Corvus coronoides, *a great shaggy throated crow with an expiring call, is replaced in some south-eastern forests by the similar Forest Raven* C. tasmanicus.

Above: *When scratching for food, this great pheasant-like songbird, the Superb Lyrebird* Menura novaehollandiae, *gives little hint of its magnificent spread-tail display and song.*
Above: *The skulking Eastern Whipbird* Psophodes olivaceus *uses its explosively abrupt whistle to advertise its presence.*

Below: *The small Pilotbird* Pycnoptilus floccosus *gets its name from following the large Superb Lyrebird to benefit from its scratchings in the forest floor when hunting food.*

Above: *The White-browed Scrub-wren* Sericornis frontalis *is a small, inquisitive bird, usually scolding from low cover, but it too may follow scratching lyrebirds for food.*

Right: *The Bassian Thrush* Zoothera lunulata *relies on its pattern for ground camouflage and keeps still when alarmed.*

strength, it is a shy bird of wet eucalypt forest and thickly vegetated mountain gullies from Rockhampton to southern Victoria.

The Superb Lyrebird *Menura novaehollandiae* is another large bird which frequents the forest floor of the south-east ranges at varying altitudes but preferring the damper gullies of wet eucalypt forest. It is found from the southern edge of Queensland to southern Victoria and has been introduced to south Tasmania. Like Prince Albert's Lyrebird *M. alberti* of the rainforests, it is large, long legged, and long necked, with a long and elaborate tail. The male is about 1 metre (3¼ feet) long overall. It feeds by scratching in soft ground, forest debris, or rotten logs. It is often shy, running and leaping rapidly when disturbed, but only rarely using its wings to aid it. It roosts high in trees, tending to climb them in flying bounds from branch to branch and only flying when descending, or in downhill escape. Males, and to a lesser extent females, may break off to sing when feeding, but males also scratch up low mounds of soft earth in different parts of their territories and display from these.

The bird's tail has a thin pair of long central shafts and is composed of broad and finely filamentous feathers that can be spread as a wide fan as big as the bird itself. The two outer feathers are more solid, equally long, and beautifully curved with outward-curling tips. All the feathers are silvery white on the underside; and the whole mass is spread as an elaborate fan, raised until it arches forwards over the bird's back; as the bird sings, the whole mass quivers and shimmers. The song is loud, clear, and prolonged; the Lyrebird's own song phrases may sometimes be mixed with an extraordinary range of the mimicked songs and calls of other birds as well as a variety of odd sounds. It may carry on for about twenty minutes and, towards its climax, the bird begins to jump forwards and back with a more rhythmic song phrasing. This is to impress a female, and several may have breeding territories of their own around the mounds of one male. The female builds a big domed nest, usually on a slightly raised site, and she alone rears the single young.

Left: *The beautiful little Emerald Dove* Chalcophaps indica *trots unobtrusively around under trees and scrub in search of food, and builds its nest low in the vegetation.*

Above: *A penetrating, incessantly repeated* worp *note advertises the presence of the otherwise inconspicuous ground-feeding Wonga Pigeon* Leucosarcia melanoleuca.

Another noisy ground bird of wet eucalypt forest is the Eastern Whipbird *Psophodes olivaceus*. It is about thrush sized and has short wings, a longish rounded tail, and a slight crest. It is dark-olive green in colour, with black head and underside. The throat is white with a black centre, and the black belly is mottled with white. It hunts and scratches over the forest floor, with body and head held low; and, in flight, the spread tail shows white tips. It is a skulking bird and needs noisy contact calls. There is a variety of loud whistles, but the Whipbird is best known for an antiphonal song in which the male's long, explosive, whip-crack whistle is immediately followed by a sharp double *chew-chew* from the female. It builds a bulky cup nest in thick undergrowth, and the male's share of nesting is confined to feeding the young. Its range also extends into rainforest, low dense scrub, and wet heathland. It is a sedentary species in forests from southern Queensland to Victoria, and there is a browner-coloured population in the Cooktown-Townsville rainforests of northern Queensland.

There is a small bird closely linked with the Lyrebird in the southern half of the latter's range. This is the Pilotbird *Pycnoptilus floccosus*, so called because, like the pilotfish with the sharks, it follows the larger species to pick up the small items that the other overlooks. The Pilotbird is plump and rufous brown in colour, with a paler rufous-buff face and a breast scalloped with brown. The wings are short, and the tail longish and often raised as it hops over the ground. The legs are strong. It moves rapidly and easily through undergrowth but flies weakly. It is another unobtrusive species with a noisy call, and the male's loud, ringing *guinea-a-week* call usually identifies it; unless it turns out to be a Lyrebird's imitation of it. It has other more silvery musical notes. Its

nest is an untidy domed structure looking like forest debris, built on the ground or raised a little on a bank or on fallen branches or among ferns.

The extensive scratchings of Lyrebirds encourage hangers-on, and the widespread little White-browed Scrub-wren *Sericornis frontalis* may take advantage, although it is well adapted to range for itself elsewhere. This small brown bird has white eyebrows and throat, staring, yellow-irised eyes, and small white wing bar. Some populations are browner, or streaked on the throat or breast, and four sub-species are recognized, covering a range from northern Queensland south and west to south-west Australia and into Tasmania. It skulks among low, dense undergrowth, not only in forests but in woodland and thickets elsewhere. It is suspicious and inquisitive, and usually appears suddenly, investigating and scolding intruders with a low harsh call. It has a short, clear, warbled song. The untidy domed nest is tucked into a low, well-hidden site.

In the wet mountain gullies and Antarctic Beech forests of Tasmania, the Scrub-wren is joined by the Scrub Tit *Sericornis magnus*. This bird is warmer brown in colour with a grey cheek, and white on eyebrows and underside. It hunts insects among ground vegetation and on lower branches and trunks of trees. Its calls are very like those of the Tasmanian subspecies of the White-browed Scrub-wren but its song has a distinctive *to-wee-to* call. It builds a domed nest in a low site.

The forest floor of wet eucalypt forest is the main haunt of Australia's true thrushes. Originally regarded as subspecies of the Scaly Thrush *Zoothera dauma*, they are now treated as two endemic species. Both are dark brown above and white below with blackish edges to the feathers. They seem to rely for protection on inconspicuousness, remaining still when alarmed. They prefer heavily forested areas, searching the ground for food. The nest is a stout cup tucked into a fork or crevice in a tree trunk. The Bassian Thrush *Z. lunulata*, with the more musical song, ranges from the northern Queensland coastal region around to south-east South Australia and Tasmania. The Russet-tailed Thrush *Z. heinei* occurs within this range in south Queensland and New South Wales and has a shorter russet-coloured tail, more rufous rump, and a song of two whistled notes.

There are two ground-adapted pigeons which inhabit the forest floor of wet eucalypt regions in areas of dense under-growth. The smallest is one of the most colourful Australian doves. The Emerald Dove *Chalcophaps indica* is bright, glossy green on wings and back, with a white patch on the shoulder. The body and head are purplish brown, and there are two pale grey bars across the back. The bill and feet are red. This bird also occurs in rainforest, monsoon forest, and in patches of moister forest in drier areas. It feeds mainly on the ground, on seeds, berries, and fruits, and flies fast and low between trees and shrubs. It has a low-pitched, monoto-nous *coo-coo* call; and performs a bowing display, often from a low branch. The nest is a thin twig platform in a vine or sapling fork, tree fern, or fern clump. It occurs throughout northern coastal forest and down the east side to Victoria. The same species also occurs north into south-east Asia.

The other forest pigeon is the Wonga Pigeon *Leucosarcia*

Right: *On steep slopes, the thinning forest saplings may allow more light to penetrate and a taller undergrowth develops.*

Below: *The Spotted Quail-thrush* Cinclosoma punctatum *has become adapted for terrestrial life, walking and nesting on the debris of the forest floor, and only flying for short distances.*

Above: *With its sudden bursts of loud song, the male Golden Whistler* Pachycephala pectoralis, *here nearly choking its young with a large insect, is a conspicuous forest bird.*

melanoleuca. It is so well adapted for life on the ground that it seems unlikely to have evolved originally in a forest setting. It is large, heavily built, and strong legged, with a small, neat head, rounded wings, and a smallish tail. It is blue grey in colour with a whitish face, white V on grey breast, and dark spotted belly. It walks strongly with a nodding head, and appears to do so for preference, walking both to feed and to evade predators. It flies suddenly and noisily when startled, and rests, roosts, and nests on branches. It feeds on fallen fruit, seeds, and berries, and is very fond of berries of Lantana and Lilly-pilly. It has a high-pitched, penetrating coo, a clear *worp* note uttered in long, monotonous sequences, usually from a low perch, and instantly recognizable from a distance. In display, it partly opens the wings, swings the tail end up and down with the tail spread, and makes side-to-side, false-preening head movements. The typical twig platform nest may be well up in a tree. It occurs from Mackay south to Victoria and, like the Emerald Dove, extends to rainforests and dense areas of inland scrubs.

The more open and sometimes grassy floors of dry eucalypt forest support other species. Like the Wonga Pigeon, the Spotted Quailthrush *Cinclosoma punctatum*, spends much of its time on the ground but it is more obviously related to birds of open country. It occurs in dry and wet eucalypt forest where the ground is more open and covered with leaf litter or stones. It is slender in build, with short wings and a smallish head. It is soberly coloured in warm brown and buff with a dark streak on each feather. There is a pale eyebrow stripe, the breast is grey, and the male has a black throat with a white patch on either side, while the female has a white throat with orange-buff sides. The tail is rounded and tipped with white. It usually moves in a deliberate walk, but it can run and will fly for short distances in low, undulating flight with rapid wingbeats. It feeds on insects and other small creatures including young lizards; it may hold food down with one foot while it dismembers it. The bird also eats seeds. The call is a thin, high-pitched *seep* and the song is a loud, penetrating double whistle, both of them of a type which makes it very difficult to locate the bird. The nest is a shallow cup of twigs and leaves on the ground, located in the

Above: *The White-breasted Robin* Eopsaltria georgiana.
Right: *The beautiful intricate feather patterns of the White-throated Nightjar* Caprimulgus mysticalis *help to camouflage it.*

shelter of a rock, stump, or grass tuft.

The other inhabitants of open forest floors strewn with dead leaves and twigs are the nightjars. These long-winged, long-tailed birds have bills that open into huge wide gapes, and they also have big, dark eyes. They hunt at night in easy buoyant flight, swooping around erratically to snatch moths and other insects on the wing. By day, they rest on the ground, and the plumage is beautifully and subtly mottled in greys and browns to camouflage them among the leaf litter. The big eyes close to slits even when the birds are awake, and white throat markings break up the outline of the head also helping to conceal them. They make no nest, but lay one or two eggs on the open ground, hidden by the incubating parents. The downy young are moved to a new site if disturbed.

The White-throated Nightjar *Caprimulgus mysticalis* lives on the drier ridges of the ranges from Cape York to Victoria. It is mainly dark, with a buff belly, and a white patch on either side of the throat. Its nocturnal song is an accelerating and rising series of abrupt *kook* notes.

The smaller Large-tailed or White-tailed Nightjar *C. macrurus* prefers similar open ground sites on moister, warmer edges of rainforest and mangroves and wetter lowland forest from Arnhem Land to about Gin Gin in Queensland. The mottling of its plumage is more varied, and it has a white throat band, and white tips to a tail which is half white on the underside. At night, it tends to hawk from a perch, from which it also sings a long series of loud, dull, chopping notes, like an axe on wood.

The lower shrub layers of forest have their songbird species, the most musical of which is perhaps the Golden Whistler *Pachycephala pectoralis*. The male's song is varied; some phrases consist of just a series of softer piping notes, but, more typically, there are four or five loud, clear whistles followed by an astonishingly loud note cut off with a whip-crack suddenness. It sings from trees and tall shrubs where it hunts for insects in slow and careful fashion on branches and foliage. It also takes berries. The male is bright yellow

Above left: *The Eastern Yellow Robin* Eopsaltria australis, *like others of its genus, favours the lower shady areas of forest cover, swooping down from tree trunks or from twigs for insects.*
Left: *The Striated Thornbill* Acanthiza lineata *is a tiny insect hunter of the upper forest foliage.*
Above: *The Buff-rumped Thornbill* Acanthiza reguloides *hunts the lower forest vegetation for insects, and nests at ground level.*

on his underside and nape, green on his back, and has a black head and white throat bordered by a narrow black band. The female is greyish brown with a faint wing bar and variable greenish and buffish tints, sometimes with yellow on the undertail coverts. It ranges throughout the forests and woodlands of the south, from Shark Bay to the south coast, and from the Eyre Peninsula to north-west Queensland. Its cup nest is placed in the fork of a sapling or tall shrub.

In the south-west, the denser forest thickets are the haunts of the White-breasted Robin *Eopsaltria georgiana*, a species of the yellow robins that has adapted to this limited habitat and which shows their typical tendency to become less yellow in the west. It takes most of its food, mainly insects, from the ground, watching from a twig or clinging to the side of a sapling or tree trunk. It is pale grey above and white below, with whitish brow and tail tips. It is vocally rather quiet, with an abrupt, whistled double note, and small pipings as well as harsher calls. The loose cup nest is often in a low site, in a shrub fork or among ferns.

Some small thornbills also occur, eagerly and fussily searching the foliage and branches for insects. The Buff-rumped Thornbill *Acanthiza reguloides* hunts among shrubs, lower branches, and on the trunks of trees, as well on the ground in drier forests and woodlands of the east and south-east. It builds its untidy domed nest on the ground. It has a tinkling musical rattle on two alternating notes as both song and contact call. It is dull olive brown in colour with a buff rump which is noticeable in its bouncy rapid flight. The underside and face are pale with darker forehead scalloping. It is replaced in the extreme south-west by the Western Thornbill *A. inornata* that lacks the buff rump but is otherwise similar in habitat, habits, and voice.

In the south-east, the Striated Thornbill *A. lineata* shares its more limited range with the Buff-rumped Thornbill but usually keeps to the higher branches of trees, searching, picking, and sometimes hovering in the foliage, often in

Above: *Seen in its typical posture, the White-throated Treecreeper* Climacteris leucophaea *spirals up tree trunks and branches, hunting insects. It builds its nest in a tree cavity.*
Below: *Although it feeds high among the leaves, the little Spotted Pardalote* Pardalotus punctatus *makes a ground nest burrow.*

small parties. It is limited to the wet and dry eucalypt forests. Its call is a soft, single or double *zit* note, and the song a subdued, high-pitched trill. It is warm brown in colour with faint white streaking on face and forehead, and dark streaking on its white breast. Its rounded nest is suspended from small outer twigs in foliage, sometimes high up. The entrance at the side has a hooded or spout-like surround.

The White-throated Treecreeper *Climacteris leucophaea* is more closely linked with the middle levels of the forests. Slenderly built, it has a thin bill and large, strong feet with long claws. It clambers on tree trunks and on branches gripping only with the feet, in a sidling fashion with one foot ahead of the other. It does not go head-first downwards, but can clamber along upside down on the undersides of branches. It flies with quick wingbeats and swoops from high in one tree to the base of another, then spirals up it; probing crevices and loose bark in search of insects. It is dark olive brown above and white below, with dark edges to the flank feathers and a reddish ear spot on the female. In flight, it shows a long buff stripe along the dark wings, and a broad dark band on the greyish tail. It has shrill whistling and chattering calls, and a series of loud piping notes. Its nest is built in a tree hole, usually in a hollow branch. It occurs throughout wet eucalypt forest, rainforest, and into Brigalow and drier tall woodland and scrub, from mid-eastern Queensland to south Victoria, and inland around Adelaide, with a subspecies in Atherton Tableland rainforest.

In the high foliage of the forest trees, birds may feed on insects, nectar, or gum nuts. One of the insect eaters is the Spotted Pardalote *Pardalotus punctatus*, a tiny, stubby billed, short-tailed bird. It is brown with black on its head, rump, and tail; the whole upperside is spotted white except for the red rump. There is a white eyebrow stripe, grey cheek, and the male has a deep-yellow throat. This bright pattern camouflages the bird among the leaves, and it is the constant loud *sleep-bab-ee* call, or a single penetrating note that advertises its presence. In winter, it often feeds in company with other small birds. It has a preference for scale insects. Although it feeds high, it nests low in a burrow up to 60 centimetres (2 feet) long that it excavates in a bank on the

Above: *The Bell Miner* Manorhina melanophrys *breeds in territory holding groups and a number of adults helps feed the young.*
Below: *The slender upper mandible of the Red-capped Parrot* Purpureicephalus spurius *of the south-west is designed to extract seeds from the gum nuts of the Marri Tree.*

ground. It occurs from Atherton to Adelaide, and in Tasmania and the south-west.

Although many honeyeaters feed on eucalypt nectar as they pass through, few are associated solely with forest. The Bell Miner *Manorhina melanophrys* is one of the stouter-billed, heavier species that eats more insects than nectar. It occurs in fairly dense colonies in limited areas of forest. It is olive green in colour, lighter below, and has a small red skin

patch behind the eye, pale-green patch between eye and bill, and orange-yellow bill and legs; it is dull enough to be lost among the foliage were it not for the voice. The call is a metallic *tink-tink*, varying in pitch between individuals to produce a musical, if monotonous, tinkling chorus from a colony. Other calls are complaining or harsh repeated notes. The birds are noisy and aggressive in defence of colonies which are also defended against other colony groups. Mating may be promiscuous, and certainly adults other than parents feed the young in the nests which are slung between twigs in trees within the colony territory. The range is from south-east Queensland to Melbourne.

Forest has its share of parrots, particularly nectar feeders. The tiny Little Lorikeet *Glossopsitta pusilla* is green in colour with red from its forehead to its chin. It is a typical tree-top species found in the south-east from Cairns to Spencer Gulf. The birds fly fast and straight over trees or in and out of the tops, the undersides of the whirring wings showing yellowish green. They have shrill metallic screeches, and soft conversational twitters when feeding on nectar and pollen of eucalypt blossoms. They will also take seeds and fruits. They tend to prefer the areas of broken foliage canopy along watercourses, and the nest is usually in a tree hole.

The south-west has a eucalypt-seed specialist in the Red-capped Parrot *Purpureicephalus spurius*. The Marri Tree, which dominates some forests in the region, produces a hard gum nut, and the slender, elongated upper mandible of the Red-capped Parrot's bill seems just designed to extract the seeds from it. The bird also raids orchards for fruit and comes to the ground for grass seed. The male is brightly coloured with a red cap and undertail coverts, green back and tail, yellow-green cheeks and rump, and violet-blue breast and belly. Immatures and females are mainly green. In spite of the colours, they are inconspicuous in trees.

Specialists apart, however, nectar and pollen are the main food supplies of the eucalypt forest canopy and, in addition to the species mentioned, this habitat may be used by no less than seventeen other honeyeaters and six lorikeets that also occur in other types of vegetation as their main habitats.

6
Woodlands

Woodland is one of the most widespread and variable habitats for Australian birds. For most purposes, it can be defined as regions where tree growth is of a kind in which the height of the trunk is less than that of the mass of foliage that it supports. It grows on drier ground than forests and, because each tree needs more root space and is shorter than those of trees in forests, the canopy tends to be more open and broken, and there are more plants at ground level.

Various types of woodland occupy a great crescent over much of the land from the coast to the dry interior, inland of the forest zones where these are present. It extends from the Kimberleys in the north-west, around the north and east down to Victoria and south-eastern South Australia; there is also an isolated area in the south-west, tapering up to Shark Bay. These areas contained grasses and smaller trees so that the early settlers were easily able partly or wholly to clear them for grazing for their livestock. A lot of it has become grazing land with a few scattered trees. The zones form a double crescent, one within the other. The outer zone has more moist woodland. In the north it consists of tropical, mainly eucalyptus woodland with the ground layer dominated by tall grasses. South of southern Queensland, there is temperate woodland, usually of eucalypts but with Native Pine or Belah important in some regions. Short grasses and herbage form the main ground cover in the south-east, but shrubs are more frequent in the south-west.

Inland of this zone are the semi-arid woodlands; these are more open and the trees are more varied, including Tea-tree and Boree. The shrub layer may be up to 6 to 9 metres (20 to 30 feet) high with undershrubs at up to 3 metres (10 feet); and there is a variable amount of grass and herbs. These woodlands merge into arid woodland with trees about 8 metres (26 feet) high. Drier woodlands have a greater variety of tree species, with different ones dominant in the various areas, and fewer shrubs.

Almost a quarter of Australia's landbirds are well adapted for life in woodland, and nearly two-thirds of them may range through it as a part of their normal choice of habitats. It therefore has a large and varied bird fauna, much of which is not closely tied to any one part of it.

The more open kind of woodland, where there are plenty of perches and where prey can be seen more easily, attracts dayflying birds of prey. Birds, such as the Collared Sparrowhawk mentioned in the first chapter, and the very similar but larger Brown Goshawk *Accipiter fasciatus*, find that woodlands are rewarding areas in which to hunt. The Grey Goshawk *A. novaehollandiae* is typically a pale-grey bird, whitish on the underside and, as in all the accipiters, as well as in most other birds of prey, the female is larger than the male. It hunts in woodland, forest, and rainforest, relying on speed and surprise to catch its prey, it prefers areas where watercourses provide avenues through the trees. It has shrill, piping calls. The stick nest cup is built high in a tree. One form of the Grey Goshawk has pure white plumage. It usually occurs in more open woodland where its conspicuousness would seem to be a disadvantage, but it has been discovered that its similarity to a white cockatoo in flight enables the bird to get close to its prey; it sometimes even stays close to cockatoo flocks.

Unlike the goshawks which feed mainly on birds, the Little Eagle *Hieraeetus morphnus* hunts mainly small mammals; rabbits are high on the list of its prey but reptiles and even insects are also taken. The eagle is no larger than a goshawk. In the more open woodland, it watches for victims from a branch or soars over open areas. It is stoutly built, brown and buff or dark brown in colour, and has feathered legs. There is a W-shaped, pale band across the underwings to be seen in flight. It has a soft whistling call consisting of several notes. It is a good flier, often soaring high on thermal currents and the male displays with a series of switchback swoops. It builds a large stick nest in a tree, or uses old nests of other large birds.

In contrast, the Whistling Kite *Haliastur sphenurus* is largely a scavenger. It is about the same size as the Little Eagle and soars over open country and in woodland throughout most of Australia. Superficially resembling the Little Eagle, it is slightly longer winged and longer tailed, and there is a small pale patch on the underside of the primaries. It soars and glides for long periods, watching for dead birds, mammals, reptiles, or fish; taking road casualties on busy road; and killing smaller or weaker animals. A number may gather at a good food source. It is an agile flier, able to snatch floating food from water, where it occurs most often. It builds a stick nest high in a tree, and breeding appears to be linked to food supply. The call is a downward-slurred whistle followed by a rapid ascending series of short notes.

Australia lacks the large, scavenging vultures of other continents. The Whistling Kite is one of the smaller species taking on this role, and the Wedge-tailed Eagle *Aquila audax* probably the largest. This bird occurs in many habitats through Australia, including open woodland where it can see its prey during its slow soaring and circling flight, and where it can build its great stick platform of a nest in a tree. Its rather weak, whistling calls hardly seem in accord with its size. It will feed on carcasses of kangaroos or cattle, and also kills kangaroos, rabbits, larger lizards, and birds.

Left: *Unlike forest, the trees of woodland have proportionally smaller trunks and more foliage. They are often more open at ground level, with grass and herbage.*

Above: *The Little Eagle* Hieraeetus morphnus *is a small but fierce hunter of more open woodland. The pale form is shown here.*
Right: *The Grey Goshawk* Accipiter novaehollandiae *has both grey and white forms, often showing some difference in hunting, but here forming a pair – the white bird is the female.*

Woodland has its share of night hunters. It is the main habitat of the so-called Barking Owl *Ninox connivens*. This is intermediate in size between the widespread Boobook Owl mentioned in the second chapter, and the big Powerful Owl *N. strenua* of the forests; it is similar to both birds in its habits. It has a loud *wook-wook* barking call, and rarely may use a high-pitched, tremulous scream. The Barking Owl shares the woodland with two barn owls. The typical Barn Owl *Tyto alba*, widespread throughout Australia, is distinguished by the big discs of stiff feathers around the dark eyes that give it a heart-shaped face. It is mostly white, with grey and buff on the back, and finely mottled with black-and-white marks. It is long winged, and has an easy, drifting flight; it watches the ground below in flight or from a perch, soundlessly pouncing on small animals. In some areas its numbers appear to be closely linked to fluctuations in small rodent populations. It has a long, thin, quavering screech and, at the nest, uses snoring and hissing calls. The nest is made in a cavity in a tree, among rocks, or on a building. A second, very similar, but much larger barn owl may also occur. The Masked Owl *T. novaehollandiae* is browner than the Barn Owl on its face and body. Although it is widespread, the bird is not found in the drier areas of central and western Australia. Its habits are also similar to the Barn Owl's but it does not occur around buildings so often. Its screech is a similar but more rasping call. It takes larger prey – up to rabbits in size.

Another quite large night hunter is the Tawny Frogmouth *Podargus strigoides*. It resembles a big, large-headed nightjar, with plumage that is very finely mottled and streaked in brownish grey. Unlike a nightjar, it tends to perch with a fairly upright position. The big, staring eyes have yellow irises, the bill is blunt, stout and broad but it is small compared with the head-splitting gape revealed when it is opened fully. By day it tends to rest on dead timber, often at the end of a broken branch or stump, with plumage sleeked,

Above: *Lacking competition, the Wedge-tailed Eagle* Aquila audax *may be a powerful hunter or a carrion eater. Rabbits are typical prey, but it will feed on dead sheep or kangaroos.*
Below: *The Whistling Kite* Haliastur sphenurus *is the widespread soaring scavenger of many areas.*

Above: *Biggest of the barn owls and approaching the Powerful Owl in size, this Masked Owl* Tyto novaehollandiae *crouches and raises its wings in threat.*

Above: *By night, the Tawny Frogmouth* Podargus strigoides *is a silent hunter, swooping on small creatures from a perch.*
Below: *The parent of this fluffy young Tawny Frogmouth is trying to appear to be a dead branch.*

Above: *The Kookaburra* Dacelo gigas, *alert and silent, watches to snatch and swallow any small creature.*

bill uptilted, and eyes closed to slits so that it looks like an extension of the broken wood. It keeps quite still but may be awake and alert, and will fly if it is threatened. At night, with feathers ruffled and eyes open, it looks a quite different bird. It watches from perches, swooping down with big, broad wings to snatch and swallow insects and other small creatures. Its call is a soft booming *oom*, and the nest a small twig platform in a tree fork. The bird prefers woodland but, despite this, it is widespread except in desert areas.

There is a member of the Kingfisher family, about as large as an owl or a frogmouth, which is also a widespread predator. This is the daytime-hunting Laughing Kookaburra *Dacelo gigas*. It is a big, stout-billed kingfisher that watches from a perch and swoops down to take insects, but will also eat lizards, snakes, and small birds. It is brown on its back, wings, and tail, and has a light-blue wing patch and dark tail barring. The underside and head are greyish white with a brown crown and cheeks. The Kookaburra nests in a large tree hole in which the cavity is about level with the entrance. Pairs hold permanent territories and some young may remain with the parents as helpers. They assist in caring for the young which may be dependent for several months. Helpers also assist in defending a territory, and the laughing call is used in territorial advertisement. It is a rapid, hysterical-sounding cackling, beginning with *Koo-hoo-hoo-hoo. . . .* notes changing to a faster, higher, and harsher *kaa-kaa-kaa . . .* This is used in chorus by birds defending boundaries, and is accompanied by short ritual flights by successive birds between two perches.

The Kookaburra occurs throughout the woodland of the east and south-east and it has been successfully introduced into the south-west. In forests of northern Australia, it is mainly replaced by the Blue-winged Kookaburra *D. leachii*. This bird is a little smaller with blue wings, and the male has a blue tail. The head is pale with fine dark streaks and pale-irised eyes. Its call is a higher-pitched and more rapid howling laugh.

Australian woods also hold a smaller, thrush-sized bush kingfisher. The Sacred Kingfisher *Halcyon sancta* occurs both near and well away from water. It watches from a bare twig or similar perch, swooping down for food. By water, it may take fish and crustaceans, but takes grasshoppers, beetles and other insects, small lizards, and similar creatures elsewhere. It is a blue-green colour on the crown of the head, back, and wing coverts, and still bluer on its wings and tail. The underside, throat, and a broad band round the neck are pale buff or whitish, while a dark band extends from eye to nape. There is an orange spot in front of the eye. Its typical call is a loud *ek-ek-ek-ek*. It nests in a burrow in a bank or termite nest, flying directly at it to chip off the first piece before excavating its hole. It may sometimes use hollow branches. It is also found in dry eucalypt forest, riverine forest, and mangroves, occurring across much of Australia except the dry centre; southern birds migrate northwards in winter.

Among the perching birds or passerines, the woodland predators are the butcherbirds. The Grey Butcherbird *Cracticus torquatus* is widespread except in arid desert and on Cape York. About two-thirds the size of a magpie, it is grey on the back, and greyish white on its rump and underside. The head is black with white on the throat, collar, and a spot on front of the eye. The wings and tail are black with white edges to secondaries. The tip of the tail is also white. The bill

Above: *The Grey Butcherbird* Cracticus torquatus *is more raptorial than it appears, and kills small birds, mammals, and reptiles.*
Below: *The Sacred Kingfisher* Halcyon sancta, *seen here at a nest hole in a tree termite nest, occurs in dry country as well as by water. It takes various small creatures and insects.*

is stout and tapering, and the upper mandible has a hooked tip. The bird watches for prey from a perch and then swoops on it or pursues it with rapid wingbeats. It feeds on small birds, mice, lizards, and insects. Butcherbirds use the bill to kill prey but, unlike other birds of prey, are unable to hold it in their feet to tear it up, so they try to wedge it into a tree fork or among or on thorns. The large twig nest, with its fine lining, is tucked into a tree fork. The pleasing song consists of regionally variable phrases of deep musical piping notes that may be sung as a duet by a pair. It also uses more subdued mimicry of other birds, and has high-pitched and harsh aggression and alarm calls.

In more open woodland, and in arid and cleared areas with scattered trees, the Grey Butcherbird is replaced by the Pied Butcherbird *C. nigrogularis* which has the finest calls of any Australian bird. The notes are pure, flute-like tones of high or low pitch, sometimes uttered by several birds in chorus; in its wild setting it is a most unexpected and lovely sound. In calling, the bird performs a characteristic lowering and upward thrust of the bill. Pairs will sing in duet . It is black on breast and head, and has a stout, pale-coloured bill with a dark tip. White on the underside extends up the sides of the breast to a broad white band across the nape. The wings are black with a white bar, and the rump and outer tail tips are white. In general habits, it is like the Grey Butcherbird, but the browner young remain with the adults as helpers in their first adult year.

Unexpectedly, the more open woodland is used by a large bird which belongs to a group better known as shorebirds. The Bush Stone Curlew *Burhinus magnirostris* is about the size of a domestic fowl, but has very long legs, a longish tail, a slim neck, and a disproportionately large head with big, staring eyes and a stout, stubby bill. The plumage is streakily camouflaged in grey, buff, and black, and the yellow-irised eyes are set in blackish eyestripes with white brows. The bird prefers the more open ground under trees,

Above: *The great eyes of the Bush Stone Curlew* Burhinus magnirostris, *here seen partly closed by day, enable it to hunt at dusk and after dark.*

Below: *For many, the hungry flocks and raucous voice spoil the beauty of the Sulphur-crested Cockatoo* Cacatua galerita.

where there is leaf litter and sparse, grassy herbage. It rests in the shade by day, eyes partly closed even when awake. If disturbed, it prefers to run with head held low, and may lie flat, with head and neck extended, relying on the plumage camouflage for protection – a technique also used by the downy young. If necessary, it flies strongly with slow wing-beats, showing pale wing bars and white patches. It is mainly active by night, often moving to more open places and picking up insects and other small creatures.

It communicates by noisy, far-carrying calls. These are long, mournful two-syllable whistles, rising in pitch and intensity, and often ending in lower and more rapid calls. Several birds may call in chorus. The nest is a small cleared scrape on the ground usually holding two large eggs. The chicks have woolly down and are fed for a few days before feeding themselves. It is a widespread but infrequent bird across much of Australia although it avoids areas where vegetation is either dense or scarce.

The main plant foods that forests provide for birds are fruit and flowers but, especially in open, grassy woodland, seeds supply an important food source. As a result, there are more seed-eating, ground-feeding parrots, although perhaps not as many pigeons as might have been expected. Unfortunately, the various kinds of grain plants which farmers grow are seen by birds as just different types of superior, seeding grasses even when they are as large as maize; and some species have become regarded as pests in agricultural areas.

The big Sulphur-crested Cockatoo *Cacatua galerita* is the most familiar of these. It is a white bird with a yellow wash

Left: *Beautiful against a blue sky, the Galah* Cacatua roseicapilla *seems the very emblem of Australia's outback.*

Below: *The subtle combination of colours makes the male Turquoise Parrot* Neophema pulchella, *seen here feeding its mate, the most beautiful of the little grass parakeets.*

to its underwings and tail, and a big, narrow, forward-curving crest of yellow feathers that can be erected or flattened as its mood dictates. With its raucous screeches, squawks, and whistles, it is always conspicuous. It has rounded wings and a distinctive flapping and gliding flight. It usually occurs in flocks that feed on the ground in open areas, taking seeds as well as digging for roots. They rest at midday and at night in trees, however, although they prefer isolated trees or groups of trees with bare upper branches. It nests in tree cavities, but some make burrows in river cliffs. It is a versatile animal, capable of exploiting a variety of food sources, and occurs in many different types of vegetation, wherever there are trees.

Australia's unofficial national bird is another cockatoo, the Galah *C. roseicapilla*, which has similar habits. It prefers drier areas and, although it ranges widely in Australia and into the dry heart, it is not found in moist forests. One of the smaller cockatoos, the Galah is ashy grey on its back, wings, and tail, but a deep rose pink on the face and underside; it also has a cap-like crest of whitish or pale-pink feathers. It is highly sociable and usually occurs in flocks. The Galah has a high-pitched, thin, *chill* call, and various screeches. The flight is strong and fast, appearing light and easy and, when it flies in flocks, individuals respond quickly to changes in direction so that the flock seems almost to fly in unison. Their tendency to fly in flocks, often with sudden mass tilting and wheeling so that pink undersides alternate with grey backs, makes these cockatoos a memorable part of outback scenery. Galahs nest in tree holes, often re-using them from year to year, and many pairs may nest close to one another. Fledgling young are brought together into a creche flock in a tree to await parents with food. Most of the food, consisting of ripe seeds, is taken from the ground.

Of the more typical parrots, the pale-cheeked rosellas tend to occur mainly in woodland; and, in the south-west, the

Left: *The slender Regent Parrot* Polytelis anthopeplus, *of which two males are shown, ranges into the more open riverine and paddock timber as well as into south-western woodland.*

Above: *A heavily built ground dove, the Common Bronzewing* Phaps chalcoptera *is a widespread but often overlooked species.*
Below: *The little, long-tailed Peaceful Dove* Geopelia striata *is a bird of more open woodland in drier areas, feeding on seeds in grassy places and by roadsides.*

trees, moving between them in fast easy flight, but feed mainly on the ground. They have a harsh *carrak* flight call, and softer whistles and twittering notes. The nest is often deep in a hollow tree. In addition to the western population, the species occurs on part of the river systems of inland south-east Australia.

The beautiful little grass parrots of the genus *Neophema*, also feed mainly on fallen seeds. Slender, narrow winged, and long tailed, they range through various habitats usually preferring more open places, although the lovely Turquoise Parrot *Neophema pulchella* of the south-east is very much a woodland bird, usually feeding on seeds of grass and herbs under trees. The male is bright green above, bright yellow on the underside, with a light-blue face, and the wings are varying darker shades of blue with big chestnut-red covert patches. The tail is green with yellow outer feathers which are conspicuous in flight. The female lacks the chestnut-red patch and has a paler face. It is a quiet, unobtrusive bird, feeding in pairs or little parties among the grass tufts. It can fly rapidly and directly but, when disturbed, the birds flutter more erratically for shorter distances, perching in trees when alarmed. It has a highpitched, tinkling, two-note flight call, and more subdued twittering. The nest is in a cavity of a tree or log.

The Common Bronzewing *Phaps chalcoptera* is a pigeon which inhabits woodland where seed is available, although it also occurs in more open and arid country where it relies heavily on the seeds of wattles. It is heavily built, a little larger than the domestic pigeon, and has shorter, rounded wings and a proportionately smaller head. In colour, it is mainly light browns and greys, pinker on breast and nape, with a creamy forehead and a white streak across the face. The wing coverts are mainly iridescent bronze and green. The female is similar but duller. It roosts and nests in trees and bushes but spends much of its time on the ground. It usually occurs near water, and drinks mainly just after dark and before dawn. It has a soft, deep *oom* coo, which is repeated monotonously. In display, the male bows and opens his wings a little to show the markings off to their best advantage.

Another dry-country pigeon occurring in grassy, open

Regent Parrot *Polytelis anthopeplus* inhabits it, but this bird also ranges into riverine timber and trees around paddocks. It is a slim, long-tailed bird. The male is greenish gold on its head, body, and wing coverts and the latter have a red hind border. The back is dark olive green, and the flight feathers and tail are blue-black. The female is similar but duller and greener. The bill is coral red. These birds rest and shelter in

Above: *The Purple-crowned Lorikeet* Glossopsitta porphyrocephala *is a little brush-tongued nectar feeder of the treetops.*
Below: *The vivid-coloured Rainbow Lorikeets* Trichoglossus haematodus *are greedy for nectar and have learned to come regularly to feeding places provided for them.*

Above: *The Black-chinned Honeyeater* Melithreptus gularis *can climb strongly and clamber over branches.*

Below: *The Yellow-tufted Honeyeater* Lichenostomus melanops *is a widespread species taking nectar as well as insects.*

woodland is the little Peaceful Dove *Geopelia striata*. Slender and long tailed, it is grey-brown in colour with a pinkish breast and a blackish bar on the feather tips of its back and breast. It has a high *coo-cu-coo* call. Often in small parties, these birds feed on seeds, walking and running over the ground in search of them. It builds a thin twig nest in a shady bush or tree. It has a swift undulating flight, and the display is a series of rapid bows with tail raised and fanned.

In addition to seed eaters, the nectar feeders are also present. In the east, the vulgarly vivid Rainbow Lorikeet *Trichoglossus haematodus* occurs in woodland as well as forest, feeding mainly on nectar from blossoms. Glossy plumaged and mainly green, it has a bright violet-blue head and belly, a breast grading from orange-red to yellow at the sides, and nape yellowish green. The Red-collared Lorikeet *T. rubritorques* replaces it in northern woodland and forest and has an orange nape and a black belly. Both birds are sociable, feeding in noisy flocks, screeching in flight, and chattering when perched. Flight is fast and direct, showing red-and-yellow underwings. The nest is a hole in a tree near water.

A much smaller nectar feeder, ranging from woodland into dry eucalypt forest and mallee, from the south-west to Victoria, is the little Purple-crowned Lorikeet *Glossopsitta porphyrocephala*. It has a dark purple crown patch, red-orange forehead, orange-yellow ear patch, blue wing band, red underwing, and pale blue breast. The rest of the bird is green. It is sociable and flies rapidly, small parties scurrying over and through the foliage from one food source to another. It constantly uses a shrill *tsit* note in flight, and a shrill twittering when feeding. It will also eat orchard fruit and sometimes insects as well. It wanders nomadically in search of

nectar. It nests in holes in trees.

Many honeyeaters visit woodland for nectar, but those kinds which live mainly in woods tend to eat more insects and fruit. The little Banded Honeyeater *Certhionyx pectoralis* of northern woodland and forest is a typical nectar feeder. It has a slender bill and eats mainly nectar and pollen. It is black on its crown, back, wings and tail, with some greyish markings on the back. The underside and rump are white and there is a thin black band across the breast. Immature birds are brown instead of black. It makes various small, sharp, or nasal calls and a phrase of descending notes. The cup nest is suspended in a horizontal twig fork.

The Yellow-tufted Honeyeater *Lichenostomus melanops* is bigger and its bill is blunter. It takes nectar but also hunts insects in the foliage and on branches. It is olive brown in colour with yellow edges to the wing and tail flight feathers. The bird has a black face with bright-yellow throat and ear tuft, and the top of the head is duller yellow with bristly feathering on the forehead. The belly is a pale, streaky, greenish yellow colour. It has various churring and twangy calls and some more musical notes. The cup nest is suspended in a shrub or vine tangle.

The Black-chinned Honeyeater *Melithreptus gularis* occurs throughout the woodlands and dry forests of the east and north. It is green above and pale grey below, but the head is black, and the throat is white at the sides and sooty at the centre. A white band runs from eye to eye around the back of the head, and there is a blue crescent of bare skin over the eye. In the northern half of its range, the birds have yellow on the nape and rump, and the eye crescent is pale green. It eats mainly insects and spiders, spending a lot of time searching foliage, branches, and trunks, climbing strongly as it goes. The bill is shortish and curved. It hangs the cup nest in thin twigs of outer foliage.

Bigger honeyeaters also occur. The Bell Miners *Manorina melanophrys* of the forest are replaced in eastern dry woodland by the Noisy Miner *M. melanocephala*. This has a short, stout, yellow bill and is mainly grey with a touch of yellow on the wings. The face and crown are black, with a whitish forehead, and bare yellow skin behind the eyes. It forms territory-holding colonies, with more males than females. Social behaviour is complex, including greeting displays with wing waving and open bills, accompanied by nagging calls. Predators are noisily and communally mobbed, and other birds, including harmless and smaller species, are persecuted and sometimes killed. In addition to insects and other small creatures, they eat nectar and fruit. They have peevish *pwee-pwee-pwee* calls and various nasal, mewing, and

Above: *Highly sociable and aggressive, the Noisy Miners* Manorhina melanocephala *tend to dominate and bully the smaller birds within their breeding territories.*

Above right: *The squat, short-legged Apostlebird* Struthidea cinerea *is intensely sociable in all its activities.*

chuckling notes. When breeding, they have a musical whistling dawn chorus; and displaying males climb upwards in steep flight, calling. The nest is often a flimsy cup of twigs and grasses suspended between twigs; and members of the colony work as helpers during nesting.

The friarbirds, still larger honeyeaters with strong, curved bills, also occur in woodland and into forest and swamp vegetation. The Little Friarbird *Philemon citreogularis* of the north and east is grey, paler below, and silvery on its breast and neck, with bare blue skin under the eyes. The larger Silver-crowned Friarbird *P. argenticeps* of northern areas has more spiky, silvery plumage on its breast, neck, and crown, the face being bare black skin with a red-irised eye; and there is a ridge-like knob on the top of the bill. The largest, the Noisy Friarbird *P. corniculatus* of the eastern woodlands, is the size of a pigeon and its whole head and

has a strong undulating flight. When not nesting, it often occurs in parties or small flocks. It is inquisitive, investigating all possible food sources, and it is considered to be a nuisance to fruit growers. This is an aggressive bird, noisily mobbing predators such as owls and goanna lizards.

Although it can build a typical cup nest in a tree fork, it may use old nests of other large honeyeaters; often, it makes use of deserted domed nests of the Grey-crowned Babbler *Pomatostomus temporalis*, relining them or building in them.

The Grey-crowned Babbler is one of Australia's false babblers, evolving here but bearing an uncanny resemblance to some of the typical Asian babblers of separate origin. It is the largest of its genus, similar in size to the Blue-faced Honeyeater. It is found across most of Australia except the centre and west of the southern half. It is highly sociable, living in family groups in which the younger birds help in the nesting of the dominant pair. The group defends a territory against others. The nest is a big, domed structure able to accommodate the whole group. Apart from the nest for breeding, other nests are built, and repaired, as dormitories in which the group roosts at night. New ones are built at intervals. It is such nests that the Blue-faced Honeyeaters use for themselves. The babblers move and feed as a group, usually low down, probing leaf litter and soil as well as trunks and branches with loose bark, in search of insects and small creatures. When resting, they tend to huddle together and preen each other.

They are self-assertive and inquisitive, with yodelling, antiphonal calls in which the chief female's *yah* is instantly followed by the male's *ahoo* with helpers contributing a confused background. The alarm call is a harsh *shak*, and potential predators and intruders are mobbed boldly. The bird's plumage is brownish grey, becoming blacker towards the tail end. The rounded tail is black with white tips to its outer feathers. The crown is pale grey, bordered by large white eyebrow stripes; the band across the face is blackish and the throat white. The iris of the eye is lemon yellow in adults, but brown in the young, becoming paler over several years as they mature. A buff patch shows on the wing in flight; and northern birds have a reddish-brown breast.

Woodland also offers a home to two other species with specialized nesting habits. They are the mud-nesting Apostlebird *Struthidea cinerea* and White-winged Chough *Corcorax melanorhamphos*. Both live in social groups of five to ten birds or sometimes more. Both build large, bowl-shaped mud nests on top of branches or similar supports. The mud is added at intervals in building and is reinforced with

neck are bare and black, and it has red eyes and a knobbed bill. The larger two make odd, raucous squawks and croaks, hollow throaty calls, and clanking and ringing notes, while the voice of the Little Friarbird is higher pitched and more mellow. They build deep cup nests. When not breeding, they tend to move in search of flowering trees and shrubs.

An oddity in its nesting is the Blue-faced Honeyeater *Entomyzon cyanotis* of the north and east. This looks like a giant member of the Black-chinned Honeyeater group *Melithreptus*, but it is as big as a Noisy Friarbird. It inhabits eucalypt forests. This honeyeater is golden olive above, white below, with a white-banded black head; but the bare patch of bright-blue skin extends above and behind the eye to form a large face patch. It feeds on fruit, insects, and nectar. It is agile and acrobatic, climbing and clinging on to tree trunks and branches, and snatching insects in mid-air. It

Below left: One of the big, bald-headed honeyeaters, the Noisy Friarbird Philemon carunculatus *feeds mainly on nectar from trees or shrubs, such as this Grevillea.*

Below: The Blue-faced Honeyeater Entomyzon cyanotis *often uses nests of other species when breeding.*

grass or with similar fibres. There is a softer lining of plant material. Both species are exceptional in that, during their communal nesting, more than one female may lay in the nest, the whole group incubating eggs and rearing young. It appears that there is one dominant male controlling the group.

Apostlebirds are squat and stout looking, and have a deep but stubby bill. They are dark grey in colour, browner on the wings and blacker on the tail. They spend much of the time searching for food on the ground and, although they seem short legged, they run and walk with rapid strides. They fly rather heavily and low to the ground, with intermittent glides. The birds rest and roost huddled on a branch. They can hop, and they leap between branches partly spreading their wings and tail. The voice is harsh and grating, consisting of various short calls, *ch-kew*, *creechew*, and a nasal *git-out* when annoyed. They are noisy and aggressive and will mob and attack intruders. Apostlebirds occur mainly in the east, from the Gulf of Carpentaria southwards, and inland in north Northern Territory. They also range into Brigalow, Native Pine, and drier scrub, usually occurring near water.

White-winged Choughs are more slender and longer-legged than Apostlebirds. They have thin, curved bills. At times, they tend to fluff up the plumage to give a larger, laterally flattened appearance. A white patch can be seen on the wing when it is spread in flight. The iris of the eye is red; this is emphasized when the pupil becomes smaller if the bird is excited. The iris is brown in young birds and, as in the babblers, this feature gives a clue to an individual's maturity. The group usually spreads out over the ground, probing leaf litter and soft ground for food, but they all rush together when something is discovered. They react to swooping magpies or to other attackers by clumping together on the ground, waving black-and-white wings, gaping, eyes flashing, and screaming defiance. More typical calls are mournful whistles and piping sounds. They roost above ground, and the nest may be high in a tree.

Woodland has a generous share of insect-eating birds, including flycatchers, robins, warblers, and thornbills. The biggest of the perching insect catchers is probably the Dollarbird *Eurystomus orientalis*. It occurs as far north as Asia where it is known as the Broad-billed Roller. It is a summer migrant to Australia, wintering in New Guinea and nearby islands. It is a stout-bodied percher with small legs and feet, and it has a big head with big dark eyes and a stout red bill with a large gape. It is light blue in colour, masked on head and mantle with dark brown; it is greenish on wing coverts and back, and there is a lilac-blue patch on the

Below left: *A tiny, inquisitive insect-hunter among the leaves, the* Weebill Smicrornis brevirostris *builds a projecting entrance to its domed nest suspended among the foliage.*
Above: *The basin-like mud nest of the White-winged Chough* Corcorax melanorhamphus *straddles a horizontal branch. It is used by a communal group in which several females may lay eggs.*
Right: *The cavity-nesting Dollarbird* Eurystomus orientalis *watches from a perch and swoops down after prey with a flash of the bright blue wings.*

throat. Wing and tail flight feathers and the underwings are a vivid deep blue, and the primaries have a rounded silvery patch, the 'dollar' of the name. The tail is shortish; the wings long and broad. It watches from a perch, swooping with a flash and sweep of bright-blue wings to catch large insects in the air or to snatch them from the ground. The flight is easy, swooping, and flapping. The Dollarbird has a loud, rasping *kak-kak-kak* call and performs a high, erratic, tumbling display flight with wild calling. To hunt, the bird needs open woodland and it occupies these habitats in the north and east. The nest is a tree hole with no nest material; it may also use old kingfisher holes in tree termite nests.

At the other extreme, the smallest insect hunter is the round-headed, stubby billed Weebill *Smicrornis brevirostris*, Australia's smallest bird. It is olive brown above and creamy buff below; birds in the south show some streaking on the throat, while those in the north are olive green above and yellowish below with a plain throat. The birds are widespread over most of Australia except in thick forest or in treeless areas. They move in pairs or small parties through the trees and shrubs, often in company with other small birds, searching the leaves for insects and occasionally hovering to snatch one. They use brief, harsh *tidid* contact calls, as well as surprisingly loud clear *weebill* or *weebee* and *willy-weet, willy-weetee* songs. The birds seem indifferent to the presence of people. The nest, bound to small branches or

outer twigs, is domed with a projecting side entrance-spout near the top. There may be several broods a year.

Small parasitic cuckoos need small birds as foster parents, and the Weebill is one of the many hosts of the Shining Bronze Cuckoo *Chrysococcyx lucidus*. This cuckoo, not much bigger than a robin, is one of a group of similar species occupying Australian habitats. It occurs throughout the moister woodland and forests of the east and west sides of Australia; southern birds migrate to New Guinea in winter. It is a vivid, shining, bronze-green on its wings and back, and a duller purplish bronze on the crown and nape. The tail is duller with black-barred, white outer feathers. The whole underside is white with regular bars of bronze-brown; these are thinnest on the throat, and the face is mottled black and white. It has a narrow, cuckoo bill. It is difficult to see among leaves, where it feeds on insects, mainly caterpillars; but breeding males call from more conspicuous high perches. The song is a repeated whistled note rising slightly like that often used by someone calling a dog, and it often finishes with a longer descending note – *fee, fee, fee, fee, pee-err*. It has a fast, undulating cuckoo flight on narrow pointed wings. It lays large dull, olive-green or brownish eggs, usually singly in domed nests of small birds, laying the egg directly into the nest; it will also lay in cup nests. The young birds, which are duller in colour and lack most of the underside barring, move and migrate later than adults.

Below: *The Shining Bronze Cuckoo* Chrysococcyx lucidus *is one of several robin-sized cuckoos that parasitize small birds as foster parents; using Weebills, warblers, and wrens.*

7
Scrub: Mallee, Heath, and Mulga

In dry inland Australia, and where the arid region meets the south and west coasts, woodland cannot survive, yet trees persist even though they are stunted and scattered by the climatic and soil conditions. These trees are usually no more than 8 to 9 metres (25 to 30 feet) high but, together with the lower scrub layers, they grow as densely as conditions permit. Scrub of this kind can be divided into three basic types: dominated by eucalypts; dominated by acacias; or a mixture of the two.

The most easily recognized eucalypt scrub is Mallee, widely distributed across the arid southern regions but, in many places, totally and devastatingly cleared for grazing or wheat growing. Most eucalypts can regenerate from a woody base, and in Mallee areas, the conditions produce a multi-stemmed growth from a woody base half hidden in the ground. The general growth may be dense or open, and smaller shrubs are present, but vary considerably from one area to another, and grasses and herbage grow temporarily after rain. In dry areas, growth may be very open with spinifex grasses present at ground level. At the other extreme, the Salmon-gum areas of Western Australia are closer to open woodland.

In contrast to this, low, dense scrub also grows on poor soils in areas of higher rainfall where it creates heathland. This mainly occurs in coastal areas in the south-west and south-east. The shrubs tend to have tough or prickly leaves, and often form a dense continuous growth up to 2 or 3 metres (6½ to 10 feet) tall. There is a poor herb and grass layer. Heathland contains many flowering shrubs; in addition to acacias, there are Banksias, Hakeas, Grevillias, Leptospermums, Casuarinas, and Bottlebrushes. Similar species are present in some inland areas, grading through to Broombush and into Mallee heath and Mallee scrub.

Acacia scrub tends to occur on even drier areas and, over much of the arid interior, it occurs as a discontinuous mosaic with the arid grasslands. Mulga is the most widespread. As in Mallee, there is a variable, discontinuous low shrub layer, and there are grasses and herbs after rain; but spinifex grass hummocks are more frequent and widespread. This central dry region includes the central and western drainage area of creeks, often through more open grassland. As permanent drainage channels in areas which largely lack a drainage system, they may have water briefly in most, or some, years. Some of them are able to support a line or straggling series of eucalypts along their banks; these are important for birds in areas where there may be only scattered and small Mulga or

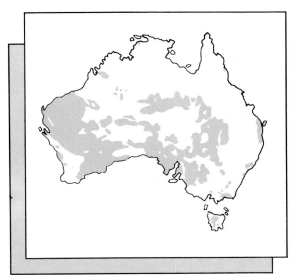

Left: *Mallee scrubland is widely distributed across the dry southern and western regions of Australia. In the more open areas between the trees grow clumps of porcupine grass.*

no trees at all. A line of white-trunked Ghost Gums against red soil and the dry yellow spinifex presents one of the more unforgettable landscapes of Australia.

For birds, the scrub vegetation offers some nectar and seeds, although these may be seasonal and this encourages nomadism. Nomadic behaviour is more likely to occur, however, in response to a lack of water. Among the insects, ants and termites become an increasingly important source of food.

Mallee has some species of birds that rely mainly on it, and the largest of these is the Mallee Fowl *Leipoa ocellata*. A heavy bodied bird about the size of a domestic fowl, with large, strong legs, it is grey bodied with a black breast stripe, and the back and wings are patterned with bronzy brown, white-edged spots. It walks deliberately and quietly, keeping still or walking away when alarmed; it flies heavily and reluctantly. It rests by day on the ground but roosts in bushes or trees. A pair maintains a territory, preferably on an area of sandy soil. The male has a deep, triple-note boom, the female a high-pitched crow. While she roams in search of food, the male tends a mound. He digs a hole, fills it by scratching in dry leaves and twigs, and then, after the autumn rains, covers it with a mound up to 5 metres (16½ feet) across and 1 metre (3¼ feet) high. The heat generated by decay is monitored by the male and maintained by constant digging or heaping of material. The female lays about twenty-four eggs at intervals, burying them in the mound and, after about seven weeks' incubation, downy chicks dig their way out and wander off. The birds feed mainly on acacia seeds, and some other seeds and insects.

The loudest voice of the Mallee is possibly possessed by Gilbert's Whistler *Pachycephala inornata*, with its far-carrying musical calls. Typical whistlers, both sexes are grey, the male with a blackish face and an orange-chestnut throat. It lives and hunts low down, taking many insects from the ground. The bulky cup nest is tucked into a low fork or thicket tangle. Its calls consist of soft, low whistles; and the song of loud whistles, clear and sweet, *pwee-pwee-pwee* calls, and crescendos of notes - *chog-chog-chog. . .* or *pew-pew-pew. . .*, the last ending like those of the Golden Whistler in an explosive *EE-chong*.

In Mallee of the south-east, it overlaps the range of the closely related Red-lored Whistler *P. rufogularis*. This bird is a little larger, and the male is more orange-rufous on the underside, throat, and between the eyes, and it lacks the dark face. It has similar calls but the song is a softer, more tuneful and loud, rising double whistle and squeak – *see-saw-sck*. It occurs in low dry Mallee with spinifex and Broombush thickets.

The Southern Scrub-robin *Drymodes brunneopygia* is a

loud-voiced, skulking bird of Mallee thickets. About the size of a Red-lored Whistler, it is dark greyish-brown in colour and has a longish, white-tipped tail and chestnut rump, faint wing bars, and a vertical dark mark across the white rim of the eye. The tail is uptilted, the legs long and springy. An insect eater, it hops rapidly over the ground among the shrubs and stems, making short flights. When alarmed, it tends to keep branches and stems between itself and the observer and has a low, croaking alarm note; at other times, it may be inquisitive. Its loud musical call is a clear short phrase – *chee-to-kwee, chip-pip-er-eee* or similar variants. Apart from its voice, it is unobtrusive. The nest is a cup in a ground hollow by a fallen branch or trunk, built up with longer twigs around the rim; there is only a single egg. It occurs in Mallee and sandplain country of the south-west, and in south-eastern Mallee west to the Eyre Peninsula.

A still smaller songster is the Shy Hylacola or Mallee Heathwren *Sericornis cautus*, a small, skulking bird of the scrubwren group. It, too, has a rufous rump but it is olive brown in colour with bright chestnut on the wings. It has the Scrubwrens' white eyebrow, trace of white under the eye, and white mark on the angle of the wing. The pale underside has dark striping.

It keeps low, moving among thick vegetation in search of insects, hopping over the ground with tail cocked high; it will sing from the top of a low bush. It calls with sharp notes when alarmed, has a persistent call of *chee-chee-chick-a-dee*, and a louder and more varied, warbling song with some mimicry of other species. The domed nest with its spout-like side entrance is placed on or just above the ground in the base of a shrub or low prickly growth.

The Chestnut Quail-thrush *Cinclosoma castonotum* is an almost ground-dwelling species of Mallee, extending into other dry scrub, more open heathland, and open woodland. It is olive brown in colour with chestnut across the lower back and rump. The wing coverts are spotted with white, and the tail white tipped. There is a white eyebrow stripe back to the nape and a bolder one bordering the throat. The throat and breast are glossy black on the male, and light grey on the female; the belly is white. This species occurs in pairs or in

Above: *Two Mallee Fowl* Leipoa ocellata *stand on the edge of a hollowed-out mound which the male has made in the Mallee scrub.*

Below: *The male Gilbert's Whistler* Pachycephala inornata *perching on the edge of its nest is the loudest singer in Mallee.*

Above: *Skulking through low Mallee thickets, the ground-hopping, ground-nesting Southern Scrub-robin* Drymodes brunneopygia *advertises its presence with short musical song phrases.*

Above: *A migrant in search of nectar-rich blossoms, the Pied Honeyeater* Certhionyx variegatus *is a bird of arid acacia scrub, and the male shows off his bold pied plumage in a towering display flight, singing as he glides down with spread tail.*

small parties, walking about and picking up insects and seeds. If it must, it flies low for a short distance, in jerky, undulating flight with whirring wings. Its calls are thin, high pitched, and difficult to hear, and the song is a repeated piping whistle that may become a trill. In display, it ruffles the plumage, lifts the wings a little, and spreads the tail to show all the patterns. Like the Scrub-robin, its nest is on the ground in a small scrape, sheltered by a bush, branch, or grass tuft; it lays two eggs.

The foliage of Mallee eucalypts provides feeding for one of the stubby billed, insect-eating pardalotes. The Yellow rumped Pardalote *Pardalotus xanthopygius* is very like the Spotted Pardalote of forests; it is whitish below, and grey above with black cap, wings, and tail. Its upper parts have white spots on the tips of the feathers and there is a white eyebrow. The throat and rump are bright yellow, the latter with a touch of red at the rear. It hunts insects among the leaves but, to nest, it tunnels down diagonally in level sandy ground, building a domed nest in the end of the tunnel. It has a plaintive *wee-wee* call.

Eucalypt blossoms also attract honeyeaters, and Mallee has at least three species that feed on nectar and insects. The Pied Honeyeater *Certhionyx variegatus* also occurs in arid acacia scrub over much of the drier regions. It has a fairly long, strong, slightly curved bill. The male is mostly black, with white lower breast and belly, streaky white rump, and white outer tail feathers. There is a white band across the wing and a small blue bare wattle under the eye. The female is light brown instead of black. This species migrates from the south of its range, occurring in flocks, but nesting in pairs. In general it is quiet and unobtrusive but the displaying male flutters up steeply in display and glides down with fanned tail uttering a piercing, drawn-out *te-titee-tee-tee* song. The nest is a stout cup in a shrub or tree fork; it is made of grass, twigs, and spiders' webs.

Two of the slenderly built honeyeaters with prominent

Above: *The Shy Hylacola* Sericornis cautus *keeps low in shrubby growth and nests near the ground, but mounts to a bush top to sing its short song phrase.*

Above: *The Tawny-crowned Honeyeater* Phylidonyris melanops *is a bird of heath and Mallee, nesting on the ground, but, like the Pied Honeyeater, towering up in display flight.*
Below: *Brightest of the heath honeyeaters, the White-cheeked Honeyeater* P. nigra *seems to need only a short display flight.*

yellow tufts behind the cheeks are found in Mallee. The Purple-gaped Honeyeater *Lichenostomus cratitus* is grey with an olive-yellow wash on the back. The face is blackish, the cheek tuft only yellow at the tip. There is a yellow stripe bordering the throat and a narrow line of purple skin above it at the gape. It is limited in its distribution in the south-west and the south-eastern Mallee. It feeds quietly and unobtrusively and, in addition to nectar, takes many insects from leaves and by probing behind loose bark. It has various harsh chirping, clicking, and chattering notes. Its cup nest is slung in a twig fork.

The more widely distributed Yellow-plumed Honeyeater *L. ornata* is greyish brown, with a yellow wash on the wings, and brown streaked on the pale underside. The head is olive, the tufts bright yellow. It is territorial, active, and conspicuous; when it is not nesting, it may be migratory or nomadic, occurring in the river gums and shrubs of more arid areas. The call is a liquid, loud *jo-jo-hik*, with an emphatic last note; and in its display flight, it towers up to 15 metres (50 feet) and then plunges down, using a repetitive version of the call. It also has a *chickwididee* call and a hard alarm rattle. The cup nest is slung in outer twigs among foliage.

Honeyeaters with towering display flights are also characteristic of heathland. Such areas are used seasonally by many species when shrubs are in flower, but some species are closely linked to them. The Tawny-crowned Honeyeater *Phylidonyris melanops* of the south-east and south-west heath and Mallee, is a slenderly built bird with a thin, longish, curved bill. It is able to probe for nectar in the big, cone-like flower heads of Banksia with their tight-packed, wiry masses of orange, yellow, or frosted flowers, as well as in similar blossoms. On more open heath, it hunts for insects in low bushes or on the ground. It is light brown with whitish breast, inconspicuous except for a tawny crown, white eyebrow stripes, and a blackish band across the face and curving down the sides of the breast. In display, it flies up in a steep slant to about 60 metres (200 feet) and hovers, singing with spread wings, and then drops. The song is a repeated, rapid, rising note which is high pitched and slightly metallic. It will also sing from a bush. The cup nest, suspended in upright stems is placed low in a bush or herbage, or on the ground.

The White-cheeked Honeyeater *P. nigra* is streaky black above and white with black streaks below; it has bright-yellow feather edges on its wings and tail. The black head has a large white cheek patch, and there are white borders to the crown. It breeds on more open heath in loose colonies, where several males may perform almost simultaneous song flights. They flutter up with rapid chattering *twee-eee* calls and hover momentarily before fluttering down again. Its calls include a squeaky *chip-chew, chippi-chew* and sharp, single or double *chips*. The cup nest is placed in a low shrub. Birds tend to be sociable and locally nomadic. They occur on heaths and into woodland with low shrubby growth down the eastern side of Australia and in the south-west.

In taller scrub and woodland, *P. nigra* is replaced by the New Holland Honeyeater *P. novaehollandiae*. This bird is very similar, but the black head has a small white cheek tuft, short brow mark, and a small moustachial streak; the iris of the eye is white. It is found in the south-west, and from

Below: The Purple-gaped Honeyeater Lichenostomus cratitus *is an unobtrusive species of tufted honeyeater with a limited range in the south-west and in south-eastern Mallee.*

Above: One of the brighter of these small furtive birds, the Painted Buttonquail Turnix varia *skulks and scratches among low vegetation, preferring to run rather than fly.*

Top left: *Smaller and darker than the Common Bronzewing, the Brush Bronzewing* Phaps elegans *of drier scrub shows the iridescent wing feathers that give it its name.*
Bottom left: *The Red-eared Firetail* Emblema oculata *is a scarce and inconspicuous grassfinch of dense heathland. It has a sad call.*
Above: *The Ground Parrot* Pezoporus wallicus *is adapted for life on the drier parts of heathland swamps; it has camouflaged plumage, longer legs for running, and large eyes for night feeding. It is rather silent and furtive in its behaviour.*

the Eyre Peninsula to south-east Queensland, and in Tasmania. It is more sociable than the last species; and its song flight is barely apparent. It has a *tchik* call, and various short whistles and harsh notes. It nests in shrubs or in low trees.

Heathland has its share of ground-feeding seed eaters. The Painted Buttonquail *Turnix varia* is a quail-like bird about the size of a thrush. It creeps through the low vegetation of heaths, Mallee, and open woodland and forest of the south-west, and from the Eyre Peninsula to north-east Queensland. It is barred chestnut and black in colour, with white streaking on its crown, back, wings, and flanks; it is greyish with white spotting on its face and breast. Almost tailless, it has a strong, tapering bill, and the iris of the eye is red. It feeds on seeds and insects, scratching in the ground litter with strong legs and feet. It prefers to run and hide when alarmed, but it can fly fast and straight on whirring wings. The female is a little larger and more brightly

coloured than the male. She has a dominant role, mating with several males and leaving each with a nestful of eggs to incubate, and to care for the young. They are usually silent birds but the female has a low and surprisingly far-carrying, booming call.

The Brush Bronzewing *Phaps elegans* is a pigeon of coastal heaths and Mallee in the south-west and south-east, extending into the shrub layers of forest and woodland. In habits, it resembles the Common Bronzewing mentioned in the previous chapter, but it has a slightly higher *oom* call, and its nest is in low shrubs or sometimes on the ground. It is darker in colour, brown above and grey below and on the head. The forehead and crown are creamy buff; and there is deep chestnut on the throat, and a stripe through the eye, and on the nape and shoulders of the male. The secondary coverts of the wings have two rows of iridescent, purple-green feathers with pale tips.

South-west Australia has a scarce grassfinch of dense heathland and heavily vegetated gullies. The Red-eared Firetail *Emblema oculata* is brown on its head, upperparts, and upper breast and has fine, blackish vermiculations. The rest of the underparts are black, heavily spotted with white. The bill and a small cheek-patch are scarlet, and a black mask from the bill borders the eye which also has a pale-blue rim. It is sedentary, quiet, and secretive, taking mainly grass-seeds but also other seeds and insects. Its call is a mournful *oowee*. The domed nest, well up in a shrub or tree, has an entrance tunnel, making it a horizontal, bottle-shaped structure of plant stems.

Also scarce is the parrot of heathland swamps. The Ground Parrot or Swamp Parrot *Pezoporus wallicus* is about the size and build of a rosella but with longer legs. Its plumage is green, with black and yellow barring or mottling; it is more yellowy green on the underside, and has a small red forehead band. It skulks in the low vegetation of drier ridges in swamps, and among rushes and grasses. It runs easily but flies reluctantly for short distances, rising with a sudden flutter, then with alternating wing whirrs, and glides like a gamebird or ground pigeon, but on an erratic course. It is rather silent with just a few repeated, thin, bell-like notes. It is large eyed and is mainly nocturnal in its activities, feeding on the seeds of grass and herbage. The nest is a hollow on the ground, hidden in the shelter of a rush tussock or bush, or in a tussock. It occurs on scattered sites near the coast around the south-east and in Tasmania, and in one south-coast area of Western Australia.

The low scrub, from the heaths and open woodland of the south-west to the Mallee, Mulga, and Brigalow of the south and east, harbours the most vivid of the blue wrens, the Splendid Wren *Malurus splendens*. Broad headed, with a thin, upright tail, the breeding male is a stunning deep royal blue colour, with light blue on forehead, cheek, and tail, black bands across the eye, outlining the cheeks, and across the nape and breast. The eastern subspecies, The Black-backed Wren, is deeper coloured and has another black band across the lower back and mantle border. The Turquoise Wren subspecies of southern Mallee is like the last but has light blue on its head and back, and violet-blue on the throat. Males in the non-breeding eclipse plumage have brown bodies and heads. Females are always brown, with rufous around the eye and a blue-green tail. Like the Superb Wren mentioned in Chapter 2, these birds live and breed in small social groups. The male has a shrill reeling song, and small, sharp contact calls are used. They hunt insects in shrubs and on the ground, sometimes climbing into trees. The domed nest is built in a shrub.

The low, dense vegetation of heathlands, swamps, and sandplains in the south-east and south-west is the home of the tiny, furtive Southern Emu-wren *Stipiturus malachurus*. This relative of the blue wrens is a ball of loose fluffy feathering with a tail longer than head and body combined but still looking as though it had been worn away. There are six separate feathers with a thin line of filaments on either side of the shaft, as though half were missing. In view of the way it skulks these feathers are probably adapted to resist

Below: *Bluest of the blue wrens, the male of the black-backed form of the Splendid Wren* Malurus splendens *gleams like a jewel in low scrubs of the south-east. Females are dull brown.*

Right: *Widespread but rarely seen, the Southern Emu-wren* Stipiturus malachurus *is an adept skulker in grasses and ground vegetation. The seemingly worn tail feathers are natural.*

abrasion by vegetation. The bird is buff on the underside, brown with darker streaking on the back, and the male has a light-blue throat. It flies feebly, but covers the ground with rapid hops of the long legs, a family party pouring through ground vegetation like a panic of mice, the thin tails held vertically or tilted forwards. If alarmed, it tends to hide in grass or tussocks and is difficult to flush. The calls are like those of blue wrens, but higher pitched, insect-like, and difficult to hear. The domed nest is located in a shrub or among herbage near or on the ground.

In the really arid acacia scrub areas of Mulga and creek gums, the birds must make more use of the ground for feeding but they may need trees for roosting or nesting. For the Little Corella *Cacatua sanguinea*, the creek gums are often important. A small white cockatoo of similar size to the Galah, it feeds on the ground in flocks, taking weed seeds and digging for roots, backing as they dig shallow grooves for surface-rooting plants. The white plumage is usually stained reddish or brownish with earth. There is almost no crest, and the bird has a yellowish wash under wings and tail. The bases of the face and throat feathers are reddish, and a bare blue patch of skin around and below the eye gives it a pensive expression. It has a wavering, high *curruk* flight call and raucous screeches. There are other subdued,

Below: *Bourke's Parrot* Neophema Bourkii *has become more common recently.*

Above: *The Little Corella has white plumage, often stained reddish.*
Right: *Little Corellas* Cacatua sanguinea *resting in the heat.*

Above: *Best known of the parrots, the Budgerigar* Melopsittacus undulatus *inspects its nest hole.*

Below: *A fast and agile flier with a loud warbling call, the* Cockatiel Nymphicus hollandicus *is another parrot that has adapted well to captive confinement. The male is on the left.*

squeaky notes. It flies strongly and rapidly on longish wings, and flocks move to trees to rest at midday and to roost at night, with noisy squabbling. The nest is in a cavity of a tree such as a eucalypt or Baobab. In normal activities, they gradually chew out a number of such cavities, possibly for future use. Although highly sociable, they become scattered and silent when breeding.

The Cockatiel *Nymphicus hollandicus* is another parrot of creekside trees. Slenderly built, with long, narrow wings and tail and a slender upswept crest that can be laid back on the crown, it is a fast and agile flier. On the ground or perched, its ashy grey plumage makes it inconspicuous but the large white patch extending across the wing coverts of each wing becomes vividly conspicuous in flight. Equally noticeable is the loud, warbling *queel-queel* with an upward inflection, repeated in series during the flight. It takes refuge in trees when alarmed, and roosts in them, preferring high, dead branches, and tending to perch parallel with rather than across the branch. Its food is mainly seeds taken from the ground. The nest is usually in the hollow limb of a waterside eucalypt, with male and female incubating and caring for the young.

A still smaller parrot of these habitats is the Budgerigar *Melopsittacus undulatus*. Seeing it in this setting, it is difficult to believe that the parties of shrilly chirruping birds that rocket through the trees have any connection with those subdued individuals in their little cages that decorate suburban houses. Wild birds are always green, with black and yellow borders to the feathers of head, back, and wings, a yellow crown, and yellow throat with black spots and blue lateral marks. The underside and rump are light green, and the tail and wing flight feathers are blue-green. In flight the wings show a yellow wing bar. They are highly sociable birds, sometimes occurring in very large flocks which feed and drink together. They feed mainly on grass seed. They are widely distributed in the interior where there are some trees. Like most birds of hot, arid areas, they rest at midday,

Above: *Gaudy and glossy, the Scarlet-breasted Parrot* Neophema splendida *seems oddly bright for a ground-feeding bird of dry shrubby scrub. It is nomadic and infrequently seen.*

Below: *Unlike other small grass parakeets, Bourke's Parrot* N. bourkii *lacks bright green or yellow in the plumage. The big dark eyes help it to see in poor light when it flies at night.*

perching in trees. When they nest, they use tree holes, and willingly nest close together.

All these birds of arid regions have the problem of finding water. Some species may find it in food and are adapted to survive with little; but seed eaters need it and, if necessary, may travel some distance daily to drink. Distribution may depend on the availability of water, and most inland species are potentially nomadic, moving in periods of drought. Dams and boreholes for watering stock must have made a tremendous difference to the distribution and persistence of many species in the arid interior of Australia.

There are two small grass parrots that live in the more arid parts of Mulga and Mallee scrub. Both were believed to have been rare in the past, but apparent fluctuations might reflect nomadism or periodic changes in numbers typical of arid-country birds. Bourke's Parrot *Neophema bourkei* is unlike its relatives in colour. It is light grey-brown above and on the wings, with paler edges to the feathers. The face is mottled pink and white with a blue line over the eye. The breast is shell pink, deepening on the belly, and there is blue on the fore edge of the wing, flight feathers, and outer tail feathers. The female is duller. It feeds quietly and tamely on the ground and among the foliage of acacia scrub. It has a musical *chu-wee* call and a soft, twittering whistle. It has large dark eyes and is active in poor light, often visiting water after dark or before dawn. It nests in a tree hole in Acacia or Casuarina trees.

The brightest of the grass parrots is the Scarlet-breasted Parrot *Neophema splendida*. The male is bright green on the back, inner wing coverts, and mid-tail. The hind face and crown are glossy, light blue deepening to royal blue on the

Above: *The White-browed Treecreeper* Climacteris affinis *swooping away from its nest cavity shows the buff wing stripe.* Left: *At its nest hole, this view of the Owlet-nightjar* Aegotheles cristatus *shows the broad bill and forward-looking eyes that make it a more efficient nocturnal insect hunter.*

throat and forehead. The breast is scarlet, and the remainder of the underparts and outer tail feathers are bright yellow. The underwings are royal blue; the outer wing coverts are light blue. The female is a little paler with a green breast and pale-blue face. In spite of its vivid colours, it is an unobtrusive ground feeder; it is nomadic, and occurs in dry, shrubby scrub of Mallee, Mulga, and scattered trees in open places, often well away from water. In most respects, it resembles other grass parrots. The nest is in a tree hole.

Other birds have a use for tree holes in these regions. Oddest perhaps is the Owlet-nightjar *Aegotheles cristatus*. This bird is widespread in Australia but is more numerous in the arid areas. It is wholly nocturnal except for occasional sunbathing episodes, and roosts in a cavity by day; if it is disturbed, it will fly from one hole to another. About thrush sized, it resembles a small owl but it is more like a songbird in its perching posture, and in the slender legs and weak feet. Wings and tail are grey or buff, and there are darker bars which become blurred vermiculations on the body. Dark bands down the mid-forehead and through the eyes meet on the nape. The big head carries a broad, flattened bill with a slight hook, opening to a huge gape bordered with bristles. Two great dark eyes, with stiff cheek discs like those of owls, stare straight forward. It has a silent, swift flight, taking insects in the air or from the ground. Its night call is a high, repeated, loud *chirr*, sometimes heard from a hole by day. The nest is a lining of leaves in a tree hole.

A smaller hole nester is the White-browed Treecreeper *Climacteris affinis* of arid and semi-arid scrub. Like the White-throated Treecreeper of forests, it spirals up trees

Above: *From this view, the big eyes and rounded, fine-feathered head make the Owlet-nightjar look almost mammal-like.*
Above right: *The Zebra Finch* Poephila guttata *is a sociable species of arid regions within reach of a source of water.*

probing for insects, and searches among stumps and in fallen timber. As an insect eater, it survives well away from water. The shallow nest cup is placed in a tree cavity or crevice, often built up with dry dung and debris to a level base. The plumage is greyish brown, and it has a white eyebrow stripe with a reddish upper border on females. The cheeks are finely streaked with white, and the underside is dark brown and white streaked. The male has a grey breast and a small patch of black-and-white stripes on the upper breast. The upper breast feathers of the female have reddish edges. The calls are a shrill *peter-peter* and *peep* notes, and a twinkling song.

In addition to the parrots, pigeons and grassfinches feed on seeds in scrub. The Crested Pigeon *Ocyphaps lophotes* is mainly a species of open dry areas with some trees and shrubs, and within flying distance of a source of water. The extensive opening up of the land for grazing and wheat grow-

With its pink and grey, black-barred plumage, spiky crest, and whirring flight, the Crested Pigeon Ocyphaps lophotes *is the typical pigeon of the drier scrub areas.*

ing, with the retention of a few trees, has enabled this bird to spread more widely, and it occurs over much of Australia other than in forest. It is grey, with a buffish tint on the wings and back, and pink on the breast and neck. The wings are short, finely barred with black, and have a double row of white-tipped, iridescent green-and-purple feathers. There is a bare red ring around the eye, and a spiky crest, often carried vertically. The crest is laid back in flight. It walks easily and runs fast. Its flight is fast and level, rapid whirring wingbeats interspersed with short glides. When it settles, the tail is swung up vertically as though it found it difficult to stop. It feeds on seeds taken from the ground. The Crested Pigeon occurs mostly in small parties but nests in separate pairs, the thin platform nest usually placed low in a small bush. It has a display flight, unlike most ground pigeons, mounting up steeply with clattering wingbeats, then gliding back down with spread wings and tail. In bowing display, the tail is raised and fully spread, the wings lifted, and the crest flattened. It has a low *coo*, which becomes an abrupt *whoop* in alarm, and a short abrupt note in the bowing display.

The most widespread grassfinch of the arid zone is the Zebra Finch *Poephila guttata*, distributed over most of the inland regions of Australia. Like the Crested Pigeon, it needs to be near a source of water which it visits at intervals during the day and where the nagging little nasal 'toy-trumpet' call note advertises its presence. It usually occurs

in parties or in flocks, taking seed from the ground. It is a greyish-brown bird with a stout, red bill, and a vertical, black-bordered white line in front of the eye. White rump and black-and-white barred tail coverts show in flight. The male has an orange cheek patch, a black patch and black bars on the breast, and white-spotted chestnut flanks. He shows these off to the female in his swaggering courtship advances. A domed nest of dry grass is built in a bush or on any available support; breeding is usually triggered the moment rain falls. Both this species and the pigeons produce a crop secretion that enables them to rear young on their dry seed diet.

Among the slender-bodied, shorter-legged, grey-and-black cuckoo-shrikes of forest and woodland, there is one species of the arid interior, the Ground Cuckoo-shrike, which is adapted to life on the ground. It is pale grey on head, back, and breast, white with fine black bars on rump and underside, and black on wings and tail. There is a blackish face patch, and the iris of the eye is pale yellow. Similar in general build to the other species, its tail is a little longer and forked. The legs are distinctly longer, and it carries itself more horizontally. Instead of snatching insects from foliage, it walks over open ground to find them, but will also chase them in the air. The flight is less undulating, alternating flaps and glides with wings depressed; but it still flicks and shuffles each wing in turn after landing. The call is a loud *pi-yew, pi-yew* or a metallic *kee-link, kee-link*. It usually occurs in small parties and, unlike other cuckoo-shrikes, there is some evidence of social nesting with helpers. The nest is a very shallow cup of material bound to a horizontal branch with spiders' webs.

The wood swallows are strong fliers which are often nomadic or migrant in search of insects or abundant blossoms. At times, they are conspicuous in the skies of arid areas. More like a Common Starling than a swallow, wood swallows have largish, broad-browed heads with stout,

tapering, light-blue bills with dark tips. The wings are pointed and the tail square cut. They hunt flying insects on the wing, circling, soaring, and gliding, using rapid shallow wingbeats. The widespread Black-faced Wood Swallow *Artamus cinereus* of the inland areas may hover to feed, and may come to the ground, where it moves in short hops. It is ashy grey in colour with a black mask around bill and eyes, and black tail coverts and tail with two terminal white tail-tip patches.

The more nomadic species also hawk after insects, but are more frequently noted visiting blossoms for nectar. All have brush-like tips to the tongue. The wide-ranging Masked Wood Swallow *A. personatus* is more frequently seen in the west. It is dark grey above, light below, with a black face and throat patch that is narrowly margined with white. The White-browed Wood Swallow *A. superciliosus* is more a bird of the eastern half of Australia. The male is blue-grey with a darker face, white eyebrow stripe, and chestnut underside. The female is paler on its face and underside. All are rather unpredictable in occurrence. When perched, they tend to huddle in bodily contact and may fly out after insects. When roosting, they may crowd and cling in a cavity or hollow on the side of a tree, forming a close huddled mass. They all have sharp *chap, chap* calls, harsher scoldings, and some sweeter notes. Breeding appears to be very closely linked with the onset of rain, beginning rapidly in suitable conditions and sometimes abandoned if rains are inadequate.

Of the small insect eaters associated with scrub, the Grey Honeyeater *Conopophila whitei* is limited to inland arid areas of the western half. No bigger than a thornbill, it is pale grey with a white belly. It occurs in Mulga and similar scrub, feeding on insects, but also taking mistletoe berries. It has a series of about three high-pitched notes reminiscent of a White-eye's. The little cup nest is built in the twigs of outer foliage. It shares part of its range with another species of similar areas, the Slaty-backed Thornbill *Acanthiza robus-*

tirostris. This has a strong, stubby bill and hunts insects and spiders in Mulga and in salt-lake vegetation. It is slate grey on the back, blue-grey on the crown, with a bright-chestnut rump and dark wings and tail. The underside is whitish, the face white streaked. It has a *see-see* contact call, high-pitched twitters, and a harsh alarm. The domed nest is built in a small bush, low down.

One little insect-eater that contributes a sweet song to the dry inland scrubs is the Redbreast *Sericornis brunneus.* It tends to occur where scrub borders watercourses, swamps, or saltbush even when these are dry. It is an inconspicuous scrubwren, light grey-brown in colour with a paler underside and a touch of white just behind the eye. There are white outer tail tips, and the male has a small orange patch on the throat, where the female is white. The ordinary calls are twittering and chattering, but, when breeding, the male sings a prolonged, varied, and vigorous warbling song, often delivered from a high branch. The female also has a song which is less rich and varied. The domed nest is built low in a bush or hollow.

Most elusive of the scrub songs is that of the Crested Bellbird *Oreoica gutturalis.* About the size of a shrike-thrush, it sings from a high perch or from the ground where it feeds. The song is not loud for a bird of its size, and the variable key phrase is sometimes written *pan-pan-panella,* the final flourish being lower pitched and with a tone like a cow bell; it is curiously far carrying. By turning its head as it sings, the singer, like the wedgebills, imparts a ventriloquial quality, making the source difficult to locate. It is shaggy crested, with a narrow black front stripe to the crest. The forehead and throat of the male are white, and the orange-irised eye is set in a vertical black line from the crest to a broad black breast band across the buffy white underside. The female lacks face and breast markings. It feeds on the ground and low in bushes. The cup nest is built in a fork; in use, the rim is oddly ornamented with live hairy caterpillars.

Left: *The White-browed Wood Swallow* Artamus superciliosus *is one of the species that hawk insects over the scrub, their breeding closely following the occurrence of rains.*
Above: *The Crested Bellbird* Oreoica gutturalis *gets its name from the odd, soft, tolling notes of its elusive song.*
Below: *The small inconspicuous Redbreast* Sericornis brunneus *might pass unnoticed in the scrub, were it not for its prolonged warbling song.*

8
Grassland, Shrub Steppe, and Gibber

In many parts of Australia trees and shrubs gradually give way to grassland. This may be a natural occurrence through differences in rainfall and soil, but extensive changes have also been brought about by clearing and overgrazing, and many regions which now have extensive grasslands of native or introduced species may have been tree covered in the past. It is possible that Australia now has more grassland than at any time in the past. For birds there is a problem in that many of these areas are now grazed, and the shorter growth and lack of seeds that often accompany this may not be suitable for them.

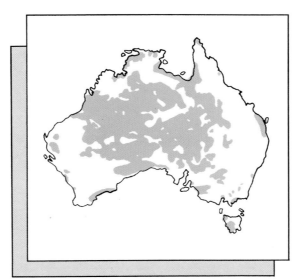

The more lush growth of grasses is on the coastal plains and lowlands of northern Australia and inland from the Gulf of Carpentaria. Elsewhere, improved grasslands replace open woodland and forest in the east, south-east, and south-west. Lush-looking but ephemeral grasses may also occur in drier areas for a short period after rain, and these can be exploited by migratory or nomadic birds.

Inland in Queensland up to the western slopes of the Great Dividing Range, and in a narrowing belt across to the Fitzroy River region of Western Australia, there are the arid tussock-grass plains. These are dominated by Mitchell grass, *Astrebla* species, which tends to grow in large-spaced tussocks with the space between occupied by other perennial grasses and, after rain, by annual grasses and herbs. Much of this zone has suffered from heavy grazing which prevents tussocks growing to any height and changes the character of the flora.

Interspersed with this arid tussock-grass habitat and extending onwards into the south-east is a zone of shrub steppe and of salt-tolerant plants. It borders and merges with the dry acacia scrub in places. A Saltbush complex of plants occupies much of the south-central region east to the Murray-Darling river system, with scattered pockets of it elsewhere through the arid zones. It occurs mainly where there is a low rainfall confined to winter, often dominated by drainage systems involving saline basins. The shrubs are well spaced with bare ground between that carries annual grasses and herbs after rain. The vegetation can include something like scrub, with Saltbush up to 3 metres (10 feet) tall, but most is less than a metre (3¼ feet) with forms of Saltbush, Bluebush, Nitrebush, and Berry Saltbush. They tend to have downy, succulent leaves and, like the grasses, can suffer from too many grazing animals. In very dry areas, they may become sparser, merging into ultimate desert while, in saltpan areas, they may grade into drought-resistant plants, such as Samphire and Iceplants.

By far the larger part of the inland region of central and western Australia, nearly a quarter of the continent, is dominated by the spinifex grasses. *Triodia* and *Plectrachne* are the dominant genera, and may form hummocks of zig-zag masses of stems up to 1.5 metres (5 feet) in diameter and 50 centimetres (20 inches) high. The bare ground between may have temporary grasses and herbs. The spinifex hummocks form a characteristic landscape, usually appearing dry and yellow but, after rain, becoming greener and thrusting up a great mass of tall seeding stems. Spinifex grasses extend into open areas among shrubs, and even in more continuous stands may have a few scattered shrubs or trees among them. Forming the masses that they do, dense but not solid, they can provide shelter and shade from the heat and sun for birds small enough to hide, or even live, within them; and for a few species they are a primary habitat.

Beyond the spinifex and Saltbush, there are the areas that contain the last sparse plants before pure desert. Where desert becomes shifting sand ridges or dunes, there may be little or nothing, but a few plants are adapted to dune conditions, surviving between the ridges. Other areas are covered by sheets of stones, producing gibber desert which may appear almost devoid of plant life but where ephemeral plants may spring up between the stones after rain.

Grassland provides a habitat for the walkers and runners which eat seeds and insects and which can exist at ground level, where there is no tall vegetation. Undoubtedly, the largest of these is the Australian Bustard *Ardeotis australis*. The male is larger than the female, and a large male may stand over 1 metre (3¼ feet) high and weigh around 15 kilograms (33 pounds). It has long, strong legs with short toes; the body is carried horizontally, the head raised on a long neck and tilted upwards in a supercilious manner. It has a black cap. The head, neck, and underside are white, with fine greyish barring and a dark breastband; the back, wings, and tail are brown, and the wing coverts mottled black and white, showing at the angle of the closed wing. It walks with a deliberate stride, watching for danger from a distance and walking away. At close approach, it will run and fly, taking off heavily but flying strongly on large wings, with neck and legs extended. It does not tolerate disturbance well.

It is a nomadic bird, usually occurring in small groups. The male displays by inflating a long, white-feathered throat pouch that droops, while long neck feathers are spread. The tail is spread and tilted forwards over the back. He swings the inflated throat pouch and makes deep roaring noises. This usually occurs on an habitually used display ground. It is otherwise a rather silent bird. The nest is a bare

Left: Despite its barren inhospitable appearance, a dry, stony gibber plain will have its bird life, such as the nest colonies of the Australian Pratincole Stiltia isabella.

scrape on the ground, and the chicks have woolly down with a complex mottled pattern. It is an easy target and quite palatable so, although it was once widespread except in the south, it is becoming scarce.

The Stubble Quail *Coturnix pectoralis* is a small, skulking gamebird which prefers the more weedy areas of grassland and thrives well on the borders of cultivation. It tends to move furtively among the grasses, running when disturbed, and, when alarmed, it rises with a sudden whirr of wings and then glides downwards to drop into cover again. It tends to live in small groups. The male's advertisement call is a clear *pippa-wheet*, or *cuck-ee-whit* piping. The nest is a scrape on the ground, hidden among grass and herbage, with vegetation pulled in to line it; Stubble Quails lay up to a dozen eggs, and numbers build up quickly in favourable seasons. Its upperparts have wavy black-and-brown barring and long, creamy streaks; and there are pale mid-crown and eyebrow stripes on the head. The male has light-chestnut cheeks and throat, and black streaks forming a black breast patch on a pale underside. The female has a whitish throat and mottled underparts. It is erratically present throughout the better areas of the east, and on the west coast; its distribution is less certain elsewhere, and it is apparently nomadic or even migratory.

Although they are not related, the buttonquails are amazingly similar to the Stubble Quail. The widespread Little Buttonquail *Turnix velox* prefers drier grassland, even ranging into spinifex. It is distinctly smaller than the Stubble Quail with an even stouter, short bill. It has the same barred and streaked plumage on its upper parts, camouflage for birds in grass, but with pale streaks at the feather edges, rather than at the centres. The breast and face are more uniformly warm brown, and the belly and throat are whitish. It has the same furtive and low-flying habits. It is often active at night. Unlike the Stubble Quail, the female is bigger, brighter, and dominant, and gives a low, moaning *oop* call. The nest is similar to the Stubble Quail's but with only four

eggs. It is nomadic, and migratory in the south.

The enigmatic Plains Wanderer *Pedionomus torquatus* is also a bird of grassland. Some claim it is a buttonquail, others suggest it is an aberrant relative of the plovers, but it also has its own peculiarities. Slightly smaller than a Stubble Quail, it has longish legs with a small hind toe, and a slender bill. Although it runs and crouches when alarmed, it usually carries itself more upright and, to gain a good view around, it will stand on tip-toe with its head held high on a narrow neck. It has peculiarly soft-textured plumage, and its flight is rather weak, fluttering, and dipping. Unlike buttonquails, it will perch on fence posts. The four big eggs are pear shaped like a plover's, and are laid in a scrape on the ground, incubated by the male who also rears the chicks. The female is polyandrous. She has a low *oom* note, but only a soft cluck has been heard from the male. The plumage is finely scalloped and vermiculated in greyish brown and buff. The cheeks are orange-buff. The upper breast is orange-chestnut, and short nape feathers make the neck look thin; there is a wide, black-and-white chequered collar. The male lacks the collar and has a paler breast. It is a bird of the native grasses, and does not seem to adapt to grazed grassland or to wheat-growing areas; consequently, it has become very rare.

Grassland also has some plovers, which are larger and broader winged than those occurring elsewhere. The Banded Plover *Vanellus tricolor* prefers drier areas where the grass is very short, and where there are bare areas bordering water. It is absent from most of northern Australia. A little larger than a thrush, it is brown on its back and wings. The head and breast are black and there is a white patch on the throat and upper breast, as well as a white band from eye to nape. The iris, the bare skin round the eye, and the bill are yellow, and there is a small, round, red wattle on either side of the forehead. The underparts, rump, and tail are white, the latter with a broad black band. In flight, the wings are black and white below, brown and black with a white stripe above. The rounded wings have a deeper, steadier beat than that of small plovers. The Banded Plover runs on the ground,

Top left: *Except perhaps for the Emu, the Australian Bustard* Ardeotis australis *is the largest of the grassland birds, striding along with typically uptilted head.*
Left: *The seemingly bright plumage of the Stubble Quail* Coturnix pectoralis *is a very efficient camouflage among grasses.*
Above: *In the small, stubby billed Little Buttonquail* Turnix velox, *as in other buttonquails, the female is bigger and brighter and it is the male that incubates the eggs and tends the young.*
Right: *As in the buttonquails, the female Plains Wanderer* Pedionomus torquatus *is the brighter bird with the pied collar.*

dipping suddenly to pick up insects. The bird's calls are loud: a metallic *er-chill-char* and harder *kew-kew-kew*. The sexes are similar and both share the nesting. The nest is a bare scrape on the ground, and the downy chicks leave soon after hatching. Parents greet intruders and predators with wild calling and swooping, and will run with an apparently injured wing to distract their attention.

The Masked Plover *V. miles* is a bigger bird, about the size of a domestic pigeon. It is longer legged and is able to cope with longer, wetter grasses. The body is white with a black tail band; the back and upper wing coverts are brown, the underwing white, and the flight feathers black above and below. There is a sharp, nasty looking, forward-projecting spur at the angle of the wing. The northern subspecies of the Masked Plover occurring from Shark Bay to Cape York has a white face with a black cap, a large yellow wattle tapering back over the yellow-irised eye, and another hanging down from eye level to below the bill. The southern Spur-winged Plover subspecies occurs throughout eastern Australia northwards, to meet the other in mid-Queensland. The black on the crown extends to the nape and sides of the breast, the upper wattle stops on the forecrown, and the hanging one is a little longer. The Masked Plover is a conspicuous, noisy, and aggressive bird, particularly in defence of nest or young. It has a piercing *kek* that can be run together as an accelerating series of *keer-kick-ke-ke-ke. . .* cries. Softer trills are used in displays. It can use most grassland except in the arid central region, and has moved into pastures and even urban grassy areas. When not nesting, they flock, and the black-and-white pattern of the rounded wings and flopping flight make them conspicuous in the air. Wintering flocks often occur by shallow water.

In summer, Australia is a winter refuge for some of the stronger-flying shorebirds of the northern hemisphere that use the grassy plains of northern Australia as well as the edges of open water. Two that do so are better known in their winter quarters in Australia than in the remote areas of

Above: *The Banded Plover* Vanellus tricolor *is the smaller of the grassland plovers, and prefers the drier, short grasses or bare places by water, where it can run and feed freely.*

Below: *The large Masked Plover* V. miles *is a longer-legged bird of wet grassland and waterside.*

Australia's only representative of a widespread family, Richard's Pipit Anthus novaeseelandiae *is a small ground songbird of open grassy places.*

Eurasia where they breed.

The Oriental Plover *Charadrius veredus* is a little smaller than the Banded Plover, but it has long slender legs, a slender body with long, tapering wings, a thin neck, and a small, neat head with longish bill; it is more like a sandpiper than a plover. In winter plumage, it is brown on its back, wings, and tail, and has a blackish tail bar. The crown is dark brown, the face pale with a dark cheek, the breast pale buff, and the underside white. In breeding plumage, the male is white on the underside and face, with a dark cheek stripe, and the breast is chestnut-orange with a black hind border. The female is a little duller. It has a loud *chip-chip-chip* call in flight, as well as melodious trills. It feeds on the ground, moving easily with head raised; bobs its head when alarmed. The flight is fast, twisting, and erratic. It arrives from Mongolia and northern China during October and departs in about March.

The Little Whimbrel *Numenius minutus* is a small, slender curlew, not much bigger than a Masked Plover. Little is known about it, or about its Siberian breeding grounds, but it may occur in thousands on the plains of north-west Australia where it has been described as the most abundant shorebird. It is mottled dark brown and buff above, and buff on the underside with dark streaks. The neck is buff, the head has a dark cap, there are pale-buff eyebrow streaks and centre crown, and a pale throat. The long, thin bill is only slightly decurved. It has a hoarse *tit-tit-tit-tit* flock call and a *tcheu-tcheu-tcheu* flight call. It walks rapidly over the ground, picking and probing; and has a light, swift flight. It usually occurs in small parties, but this bird flocks on migration. It is present from about September to April.

Relatively few songbirds appear to be adapted to open

grassland in Australia, and those that are tend to be dull, camouflaged for inconspicuousness but, by way of contrast, have very noticeable voices and song flights. Richard's Pipit *Anthus novaeseelandiae* ranges widely through the Old World, and occurs in open grassy areas over most of Australia. It can exploit the land which has been cleared for pasture and agriculture. A slender, long-legged bird with a thin bill, it has a streaky brown plumage. There is a pale eyebrow stripe, and the cheek, throat, and belly are whitish. The outer tail feathers are white and are the only conspicuous feature in its rather undulatory flight. It usually occurs in pairs or singly, walking and running over the ground in search of insects, and tending to wag the tail up and down when excited. It makes short, fluttering flights after insects in the air. It has a rasping *tswee* call and a thin, sharp *chir-rup*. In its breeding territory, the male uses low perches, and also performs a high display flight of a series of swoops with a high-pitched piercing call at each swoop. The nest is a cup on

A Siberian wader little known on its breeding ground, the slender-billed Little Whimbrel Numenius minutus *is often a numerous non-breeding visitor to northern Australia.*

the ground in a small hollow under a grass tuft.

Australia has one native lark, the Singing Bushlark *Mirafra javanica*, which also occurs as far away as Asia and Africa. It is present in the eastern half of Australia and throughout the north, in open grassland and into open woodland and scrub where grass predominates. It is rather like a female House Sparrow, with a rounded head and a stout, finch-like bill. A pale eyebrow streak extends around the back of the cheek; and the underside is plain, with limited dark streaking on the upper breast and throat. The outer tail feathers are white like those of a pipit, but the tail is short. The general plumage tint may be light or dark brown, reddish, or greyish, tending to show some match with the colour of the soil; presumably, this helps to camouflage the bird against flying predators. The effect may be aided by its habit of dust bathing in dry soil. It feeds on seeds and insects. It runs easily, but usually flies reluctantly and only for short distances with fluttering flight. The breeding male sings in flight; often mounting high in the air and hovering or slowly descending to sing. Occasionally, it may sing from a low perch. The song is prolonged and musical; it is a mixture of high-pitched trills, and deeper notes, with occasional mimicry of other birds. The ordinary call is a slurred chirrup. The nest is a cup built into a small hollow under a grass tuft; the down of the nestlings and immature plumage are mottled with buff for better concealment.

Cultivation and the opening up of new grassland offered opportunities for more larks, and a European species, the Skylark *Alauda arvensis*, has established itself in the southeast after being introduced. It is larger and longer tailed than the Bushlark, and has buffish and more heavily streaked plumage and a streaked breast. It has a pale stripe around the cheek, and a small blunt crest that it can raise on the crown. Broad wings and a white-edged tail show in the strong but slightly undulating flight. The usual call is a liquid or harsh *skirrup*. Unlike the Bushlark, it never occurs among trees, but will perch on fence posts, and will sometimes sing from them. It is the song flight for which the Sky-

Above: *The Skylark* Alauda arvensis *is an introduced bird established in the south-east. Its prolonged, often harsh and hurried song separates it from the Bushlark, as does the small crest.*

lark is famed, however. The breeding male rises slowly in a hovering flight, with wings and tail spread. He pauses at intervals and may rise to a considerable height, remain there, and then descend in a similar fashion. Throughout the flight, the bird sings incessantly, only stopping in a final plunge back to earth. The song is a throbbing cascade of phrases, sometimes piercingly shrill or harsh, sometimes

Below: *The plumage of the grassland Singing Bushlark* Mirafra javanica *often varies in tint with the soil of the locality.*

more musical and lower in pitch. In contrast, the Bushlark's song is more spasmodic and tinkling in tone. The cup nest is hidden in grass on the ground. Skylarks eat insects, seeds, and plant material.

Grass seed is a staple food for most of the grassfinches, but the majority of species prefer areas where grassland occurs with trees or water. The grasslands of the northern and eastern coastal regions are used by the Chestnut-breasted Mannikin *Lonchura castaneothorax*. It prefers the lusher growth near water, but has turned to grain and rice crops as acceptable substitutes. In the Kimberley and Arnhem Land regions, it may be joined by the similar Yellow-rumped Mannikin *L. flaviprymna* which tends to prefer drier habitats. The two species hybridize.

The Chestnut-breasted Mannikin is chestnut on the back, and a yellowish-rufous colour on its rump and tail. The head is grey with a black mask over the face and throat; the breast is chestnut with a black lower border, and the belly white. The bird has a massive stout, blue-grey bill. The Yellow-rumped Mannikin is darker brown on the back, more yellow on rump and tail, pale grey on the head, and pale buff on the breast. Both are similar in habits and feed in flocks, clinging in tall grasses. In display, the male fluffs himself up, points his open bill downwards and bobs and shakes as he forces out

The Chestnut-breasted Mannikin Lonchura castaneothorax, *a grassland bird, has earned dislike by exploiting cereal crops.*

an impassioned song of clicks, whistles, and other notes inaudible to the human ear. The ordinary call is a bell-like *teet* note. The domed nest is bound to the stems of a clump of grasses or reeds.

These tropical grasslands of the north also hide the Red-backed Wren *Malurus melanocephalus*, a little long-tailed relative of the blue wrens in which the male is black with brownish wings and a vivid crimson or tangerine-red back from shoulders to rump. Females and males in eclipse plumage are brown above, and whitish below. The sharp call notes and reeling song are a little louder than those of blue wrens, and the domed nest is hidden in a grass clump.

There is one pigeon adapted to open dry grassland, and that is the Flock Pigeon *Phaps histrionica*. Its principal range appears to have been through the Mitchell grass plains, with the main centre in the Barkly Tableland of Northern Territory. It is a long-winged species that lives and moves in close flocks. It is highly nomadic, moving frequently in search of suitable conditions. Although the range is potentially throughout northern and inland eastern Australia, it is only found on a few areas of drier inland grasses, sometimes ranging into open mulga, spinifex, or Saltbush. It requires long stretches of naturally seeding grasses, and the range has shrunk with the spread of grazing, making it infrequent and unpredictable. The male is coppery buff in colour with a blue-grey breast; it has a black head with white on the forehead, upper breast bib, and a

band around the cheek. There is a small iridescent wing patch. The female is a little duller, buffer breasted, and is brown on the head with a greyish throat and no white on the forehead. They feed in flocks in open areas and fly to water at morning and evening. The male has a bowing display like that of bronzewings and, while flying in a flock, he may glide with upraised wings for short distances, with bursts of strong wing beats between. The only calls are soft *coos*. The nest is on the ground; it is a bare scrape in the shelter of a tussock.

The low, shrubby growth of shrub steppe and Saltbush provides cover for some small insect-eating birds. The White-winged Wren *Malurus leucopterus* occurs in these regions although it also ranges through the low vegetation

Below: *This rarely seen, highly sociable Flock Pigeon* Phaps histrionica *is a ground pigeon that has varied greatly in numbers but is now a scarce bird of northern plains.*

Above: *The Red-backed Wren* Malurus melanocephalus *of northern grasslands substitutes red and black for the glossy blues of other species. The domed nest is tucked into a grass clump.*

of most of the semi-arid and arid interior. It is one of the smallest species, and females and males in eclipse plumage are sandy brown in colour with blue tails. Like other blue wrens, it lives and breeds in social groups, and these move around their territory in 'follow-my-leader' fashion. Often only the dominant male is in full plumage and conspicuously different, a vivid and glossy blue with a great snowy-white patch on each side formed by secondaries and wing coverts. It appears vulnerably obvious in such a setting. On Barrow Island and Dirk Hartog Island off the west coast, the males are black-and-white and, on the nearby mainland, sometimes they are blue-black. They have thin *prip, prip* calls, and the male has a fast, reeling song phrase. The domed nest is built low down in a bush or in grass.

This dry shrub steppe country is also the stronghold of the Australian chats. They are small songbirds with thin bills, short tails, and long legs for walking and running. Although mainly insect eaters, they have brush-like tips to their tongues and can take nectar from low-growing flowers.

The White-fronted Chat *Ephthianura albifrons* is a bird of areas of low shrubby growth, usually bordering water, although it feeds largely on the ground. The male is white on his face and underside, black on wings and tail, and light grey on the back. Black extends from the hind crown to the nape, and down the sides of the breast to form a broad band across the lower breast. The iris of the eye varies from orange to white. The female is brown on her wings and tail, greyish brown on the back and head, with white on her throat and eyebrow, and a small black breast crescent. This species usually occurs in small flocks and breeds in loose colonies. It runs and walks easily, nodding the head like a pigeon; and has a bouncing flight with quick, flipping wing-beats. It will perch on bushes and posts. The usual call is a plangent, metallic *tang*. The cup nest is built into shrubby or tussock growth near ground level; both birds share the nesting duties. In some areas, it appears to be nomadic, and is

found across the southern half of Australia.

The Crimson Chat *E. tricolor* has an extensive range over drier inland areas into both spinifex and open shrubs. It looks very different from the White-fronted Chat. The male is dark brown on his back, wings, and tail and has pale-edged flight feathers. His forehead and crown, breast, belly, and rump are bright scarlet, with a white throat and upper breast, and white undertail coverts. The female is lighter brown, with white on her throat and underside, and has red only on the rump and on a pale breast patch. The scarlet rump and black tail are conspicuous marks in flight. Its habits are similar to those of the previous species. There is greater evidence of it taking nectar from flowers. The calls are a high-pitched silvery *swee*, similar trilled notes, a soft *dik-it*, and small sharp notes and rattles. It is more nomadic in its movements, seemingly following rainfall, and breeding where conditions are suitable.

The Orange Chat *E. aurifrons* occurs in even drier areas, from Saltbush to gibber. The male is yellow with an orange-tinted head and breast and a black mask extending back to the eyes. The back is brown streaked and the wings and tail are brown with pale edges. The female is grey-brown on her head and back, with just a pale eye stripe and yellow confined to a tint on her buffish underparts. It is a sociable, nomadic bird, usually occurring in flocks, feeding largely on the ground but perching on shrubs. Like the White-fronted Chat, it has a metallic *tang* call, and a musical *chee-chee-chee* in flight. The cup nest is located in a low shrub.

Above: *The White-winged Wren* Malurus leucopterus *prefers the low vegetation of more arid regions. There is often one blue-and-white male in a party of sandy brown females and young.*

Below: *Found in low, shrubby growth near water, the White-fronted Chat* Ephthianura albifrons *occurs in sociable groups, walking and feeding on open ground.*

Among the birds which are specialized for the drier open spaces is an offshoot of the Old World warblers. This is the Brown Song-lark *Cinclorhamphus cruralis*. There are two song-larks. The smaller Rufous Song-lark *C. mathewsi* is also a grassland bird but is found in areas where there are some trees. It has a warm streaky-brown plumage and chestnut rump. The Brown Song-lark is better adapted to open Saltbush, open or lightly timbered grassland, and similar areas. It has a thin bill, longish legs, and a long tail with tapered tip. The male is distinctly larger than the female, and the more conspicuous of the two. He is sooty brown on his face and underside, fawn-brown on the crown and nape, and the upperparts, wings, and tail are dark brown with buff feather margins. The female is pale buff below with a darker belly; she is whitish on the throat and eye stripe, and brown streaked on her head and back. This species usually occurs in small groups, feeding on seeds and insects on the ground and low in shrubs. The female is unobtrusive but the male tends to perch conspicuously on tussocks, posts, or Saltbush with tail cocked. In song flight, the male circles, rising in fluttering flight and gliding at intervals with raised wings and dangling legs; he then descends in this posture, often to a perch. The song is loud, with odd metallic, guttural, and creaking notes, and may end with a musical trill and whip-crack finish. The bird may be polygamous. The nest is on the ground, a cup concealed among grass tufts; and incubation and tending the young fall to the female. It is widespread, but commoner in the south and east where it seems often to be nomadic or migratory; it is scarce in the north.

Like the shrubby growth of shrub steppe, the spinifex hummocks offer shelter to small birds. The Spinifexbird *Eremiornis carteri* is an Old World warbler that has become specialized for this habitat. Small, slender, and thin billed, it has a long tail, broad and graduated. It is plain brown above, pale-buff below, with a warmer brown crown and buff eyebrow stripe. It moves with agility up, down, and among grass stems, balancing with the long tail. Moving hurriedly across open ground, the tail is cocked, but it flies heavily with the tail seeming to drag. If alarmed, it retreats inside spinifex clumps, and appears to be uneasy in the open. Its voice betrays its presence. It has various short, sharp, and grating calls, and a subdued chattering; it also has a loud, musical *cheeriweet*, or repeated *cheerit* and *cheeroo* notes. It feeds on insects and spiders. The deep cup nest is hidden in spinifex. Although widespread in the spinifex region, its distribution is poorly known, perhaps mainly on hilly ground.

Spinifex has its own emu-wren, the Rufous-crowned Emu-wren *Stipiturus ruficeps*. It lives in spinifex, preferably where some low shrubs are also present. The domed nest is built above the ground in the middle of a spinifex clump or low bush. In almost all respects, it is similar to the Southern Emu-wren of heathland, but it is slightly smaller and, on the male, the blue colour extends from the breast to cheeks and eyebrows, and the crown of the head is a plain light-chestnut colour. It is even more skulking than the Spinifexbird, and is almost impossible to find if it does not want to be seen.

The arid regions of Australia are home to the eight species of grasswrens. They are larger and stouter than blue wrens, with long but broader tails that are not carried so high. Bills and legs are stouter; and the plumage is patterned with dark-edged white shaft streaks on the feathers. Most are about the size of a robin or sparrow but, in the sandstone escarpments of the north-west, there are two thrush-sized, chestnut-rumped black ones in very limited areas – the Black Grasswren *Amytornis housei* in a corner of the Kimberleys, and the White-throated Grasswren *A. woodwardi* on the Arnhem Land escarpment.

More widespread is the Thick-billed Grasswren *A. textilis*; it is smaller and dull brown in colour with heavy but fine pale steaks. It lives in shrub steppe country through from Western Australia to north-west New South Wales. In spinifex, it is mainly replaced by the Striated Grasswren *A. stria-*

Left: *The Crimson Chat* Ephthianura tricolor *is another species of arid areas with low, sparse vegetation. It is highly nomadic.*
Above: *Different again, the Orange Chat* E. aurifrons *occurs in the driest, barest areas. It is also sociable and nomadic.*
Below: *The Brown Song-lark* Cinclorhamphus cruralis *has a male that is distinctly bigger and darker than the female shown here, possibly polygynous, and takes no part in the nesting.*

tus which is bright chestnut-brown above and buff below with a white throat, black moustachial streak, and distinct white streaking. Both are fast-moving and highly furtive insect hunters of ground cover, hiding when alarmed in plant tufts or burrows and refusing to budge. They have high-pitched, squeaky calls, but more musical songs with short repetitive phrases. The domed nest is close to the

ground in a small shrub or spinifex clump.

Spinifex country also has a grassfinch. The Painted Finch *Emblema picta* lives on the ground among spinifex, picking up small seeds and perching on rocks instead of on twigs. It has a flattened forehead which tapers to a sharp and spitefully long bill for a grassfinch. The upper mandible is black, the lower scarlet and blue. It is dull brown on it head, back, and wings; the tail is black, the rump bright scarlet and the underside black with white-spotted flanks. The eyes have white irises, and the male has a glossy scarlet face, but the red stops short at the eyes on the female. The male also has red spots tapering down the throat and a red belly patch, but the throat is black with white spots on the female. It lives within reach of permanent water which is visited daily. Less sociable than most grassfinches, it is sedentary and usually occurs in small, loose groups of pairs, which are sporadically distributed. A domed nest is built in taller spinifex, on a basal platform of twigs and debris.

Stony or hilly spinifex country with a permanent source of water is also the home of the most gamebird-like of the pigeons, the Plumed Pigeon *Geophaps plumifera*. Small,

Above: *The spiny mounds of spinifex grass have their own warbler, the Spinifexbird* Eremiornis carteri, *a skilful skulker.*

Right: *The Thick-billed Grasswren* Amytornis textilis *is a larger, streakily plumaged relative of the blue wrens, inhabiting dry shrub steppe. Its bill is adapted to harder seeds and insects.*

plump, with short wings and tail, strong legs, and a tall, spiky, and vertically erect crest, it normally walks and runs, but flies low and for short distances only, with alternate bursts of rapid wingbeats and glides. Its colour is a warm chestnut-buff. In the east it is white bellied with a black-bordered white band across the breast; while the western subspecies is chestnut-buff on the belly with a black-and-grey line across the lower breast. The back is finely barred with black, the wings barred black and slate-grey. There is a black-bordered patch of bare red skin around the eyes, blue-grey forehead and cheek, black throat, and a puffy white band across the lower face. It lives on open ground in small parties, feeding on seeds of spinifex and short-lived grasses and herbs. It has a low-pitched *oom* call and a deep bowing display. The nest is merely a scrape on the ground, and

breeding is closely linked with rains.

Even the sparsely vegetated inland areas of gibber and sands have their bird life. The Australian Dotterel *Peltohyas australis* is a plover adapted to arid country. It is a small bird, its head and back camouflaged in a scaly brown-and-buff pattern. It has a chestnut belly patch and paler warm buff on the breast, while the throat, face, and forehead are whitish. A black band across the forecrown and down through the eye, and a black nape patch with bands down either side to meet in a V on the breast help to break up the bird's outline. By day it tends to rest among plants, squatting if alarmed, flying reluctantly but fast and low on long wings. It feeds actively at dusk and at night on insects and plants. The nest is a scrape on bare loose ground, and, when it leaves the nest, the bird kicks sand or earth over the eggs to cover them. The downy chicks may shelter in burrows. Both actions help to avoid overheating.

A similar dry-country breeder is the Australian Pratincole *Stiltia isabella*. It is migrant, some moving to open parts of northern Australia in winter but many travel as far as Borneo or Sulawesi. In summer, it occurs in open semi-arid country, mainly in the eastern half of Australia. It may use bare, gravelly edges of dams or temporary lakes, but often nests in colonies on stony gibber plains. Unlike the Australian Dotterel, however, it is usually found within 2 kilometres (1¼ miles) of water. It is slimly and elegantly built, with long, slender legs and long, narrow wings projecting well beyond the tail when folded. The neck is thin. The black-tipped red bill is short and blunt tipped. The plumage is sandy buff, with white throat and belly, and a chestnut-brown flank patch. The white tail has a black triangle on the upper surface. In flight, the thin, angled wings show black underwing coverts. It runs swiftly, catching insects on the ground, or taking them from the air in swift, buoyant flight. It has a habit of bobbing the head, and of tilting the body. The call is a musical *weeteet* or *quirri-peet*. It nests on bare, stony ground but the young take advantage of any shade.

Left: *The Striated Grasswren* Amytornis striatus *is more streaked and boldly coloured. It lives in spinifex country, skulking and nesting low in hummocks.*
Above: *The Painted Finch* Emblema picta *is a spinifex grassfinch, picking up seeds and nesting low in hummocks.*
Below: *The Plumed Pigeon* Geophaps plumifera *prefers dry, hilly country near a water source, feeding and nesting on open ground, and making only short, low flights.*

Above: *An inland, arid-country bird of open places, the Australian Dotterel* Peltohyas australis *is active at dusk and at night, relying on plumage pattern for daytime camouflage.*

Below left: *Slender, built for fast running and swift flight, the Australian Pratincole* Stiltia isabella *hawks insects in bare inland areas within flying distance of water.*

Below right: *The Gibber Bird* Ashbyia lovensis *manages to find seeds, insects, and possibly nectar on bare stony plains.*

The thornbill-sized whitefaces occur in arid country; they are tiny, stubby-billed birds which hop around like sparrows in search of seeds and insects. The Banded Whiteface *Aphelocephala nigricincta* occurs in Saltbush and spinifex of central regions. It is chestnut above and on the flanks; the front half of the face is white, the rear grey with a dark fore edge, and there is a narrow, black breast band. It has twittering calls and weak, bell-like song notes. It uses sparse Mulga or other low trees when these are present, and builds a domed nest with a long entrance tunnel low in a tree or bush.

The Chestnut-banded Whiteface *A. pectoralis* is similar in general habits, but in colour it is greyer above and has a broader chestnut breast band. It is confined to the slightly elevated gibber areas of South Australia.

There is one chat called the Gibber Bird, *Ashbyia lovensis.* It is slightly heavier in build than other chats and pale greyish brown with a touch of yellow on the face and underside. It lives on the stony plains of the Lake Eyre Basin. It runs and walks in search of food. When alarmed, it runs at first, and then takes to fast, twisting, and erratic flight. It has a display flight, mounting in upward swoops with repeated shrill *weet, weet, weet* notes to over 30 metres (100 feet), then plunging straight back to the ground. The nest is a cup in a small ground hollow, often in the shelter of a tuft or bush.

Essentially, even in the desert areas of the hot, dry heart of Australia, there is probably nowhere that is wholly without some vestige of bird life.

The whitefaces are small, stubby billed, ground-feeding birds of arid regions. The Banded Whiteface Aphelocephala nigricincta *occurs in Saltbush and spinifex.*

9
Wetlands

Australia is better known for its dryness rather than for its wetlands, and these vary considerably from one region to another. The vast drier region in the centre, extending to the central western and southern coasts has poor and unreliable rainfall. There may be no rain or, what little there is, may be confined to certain areas. Rivers are dry creeks for much of the time and lakes are saltpans. When rain does occur, it temporarily floods across country and rapidly disappears. Swamps and waterholes may hold rain for only part of the year. Heavy rain may fill lake beds; the water then evaporates and becomes increasingly saline.

A zone along the north of Australia from the Kimberleys eastwards shows the opposite situation. There is an annual wet season, in summer, when rivers flood. There are plenty of lagoons and swamps on the floodplains of rivers. There is also a winter dry season, however, in which this surface water mostly disappears. The eastern parts of Queensland and northern New South Wales, east of the Great Dividing Range, have a modified situation in which the rains are less limited to summer and the swamps and lagoons are more permanent.

Inland in the south-east, there is the extensive Murray-Darling river system. The rivers originate in the eastern highlands in areas of higher rainfall but flow for long distances across semi-arid and arid areas. These rivers are convoluted, with many meanders and billabongs. They have some permanent water and, in periods of high rainfall at the source, they flood and produce extensive temporary swamps.

In the south-west corner, and in Tasmania and the south-east from New South Wales to Victoria, the rivers and swamps may have a more assured water supply and tend to be more permanent. For waterbirds, however, these areas are prone to the greatest disturbance and to drainage.

To survive under such conditions, many species, particularly waterfowl, must be ready to begin breeding rapidly when conditions become suitable; and it is advantageous to be nomadic, able to seek out and exploit quickly local conditions which may be of a temporary or semipermanent nature. Many species that appear to have an extensive range, possibly through most of Australia, may at any particular time be surprisingly scattered and localized in distribution that is, in fact, much more limited than the overall indication of range would suggest.

Human activity has had an effect on the availability of water, just as it has affected almost every other environmental feature. In the more closely settled areas, drainage,

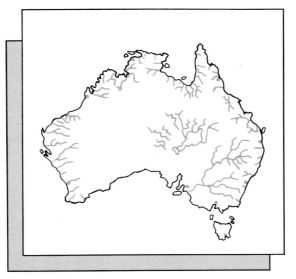

particularly of swampy areas, and the use of water for crop irrigation, has reduced what is available for wildlife. In other respects, the creation of dams and storage reservoirs has increased the availability of water in some regions where it could not be relied upon in the past.

In general, the relationship of birds to water is not so much a matter of distribution within particular climatic or regional zones, but more how the water is utilized. There are birds that live on water most of the time, requiring an assured area and depth; those that swim after food or dive for it; those that wade in shallow waters; and those that use the water margins whether they are bare or vegetated. Swamp birds are likely to be in the last two categories.

Grebes are the most aquatic of freshwater birds. The feet used to propel them under water are set so far back on the body that they can only move awkwardly on land. In water they are wholly at ease, floating with plumage puffed out, round bodied and virtually tailless; or suddenly sleeking it down and diving, staying under for a time and reappearing some distance away. The body of a grebe is streamlined, the bill dagger shaped. These birds feed on fish, but smaller species also take insects and small crayfish. The wings are narrow, with white wing bars. Taking off is difficult and, in flight, they seem to be all neck, wings, and trailing feet, although they may travel far, usually at night. The nests are masses of waterweeds, built in shallow water, or floating and anchored by stems. The bird can leap straight out on to the nest, and, when leaving, will pull weed over to cover the eggs. The downy chicks have boldly striped patterns and, when small, they may rest on the back of a swimming adult.

Australia has two small grebes and a large one. The small ones occur widely over Australia, and one is wholly native. The Hoary-headed Grebe *Podiceps poliocephalus* is grey with a pale breast and neck. The head feathers are basally black but with a mass of grey, swept-back plumes resembling well-brushed, grey hair. The iris of its eye is pale. It has a low, churring call. It prefers more open waters and will gather in large flocks. It will also nest in colonies, sometimes with Whiskered Terns *Chlidonias hybrida*.

The Little Grebe *P. ruficollis* lacks the head plumes. In winter plumage, it is brownish grey above, paler below; but, when breeding, the head, neck, and bill are blackish, with a big chestnut cheek patch and a bare yellow patch at the base of the bill. It has a loud, accelerating trill or tittering call when breeding. The sexes are similar in plumage and voice. It will tolerate much smaller waters and breeds in scattered pairs.

The Great Crested Grebe *P. cristatus* confined mainly to the east and south-west, is twice as big as the Little Grebe. It is vivid white on underside and neck, and has a white face

Left: This swamp, with its dead trees and emergent vegetation, is typical of those that provide breeding sites for waterbirds, such as the Straw-necked Ibises Carphibis spinicollis *present here.*

surrounded by two big black ear tufts and a chestnut-and-black ruff. It has complex, ritualized displays in which birds face each other and display their head plumes, wagging their heads and sometimes holding waterweed. It has a deeper *row-ah* call and other notes, but the behaviour is similar to that of the smaller species. It may nest in loose colonies.

The other underwater fish hunters are the two small cormorants which are both widespread in Australia. These rely on large, webbed feet for propulsion. They are long bodied and longish tailed with narrow, hook-tipped bills. The Little Black Cormorant *Phalacrocorax sulcirostris* is black with a thin bill. The Little Pied Cormorant *P. melanoleucos* is black above, but with white extending from its underside to the front of the neck and the face. The bill is distinctly shorter and stouter, suggesting differences in feeding. The Little Black Cormorant is a bird of inland waters, while the Little Pied extends to the sea coasts and islands. They chase fish underwater, and later spend periods perched with wings spread to dry. The Little Pied Cormorant tends to fish alone, the other often fishing co-operatively in flocks. In their strong, flapping and gliding flight, the Little Pied is more individual, the Little Black tending to move in lines and chevrons. Apart from low, guttural calls when breeding, both are mainly silent. The nests are untidy platforms of sticks and debris. The Little Black Cormorant tends to nest in trees on swamps and floodland, usually over water, forming colonies and sometimes joining with other waterbirds. The Little Pied Cormorant may use trees, bushes, or the ground for nesting. In both, nesting tends to be linked with abundant food supplies.

On the large inland water, whether permanent or temporary, that Little Black Cormorants use, they may be joined by a much larger fisher, the Australian Pelican. It is pied; white with black on rump and tail and with big white covert patches on its black wings. This species, too, may drive fish

Above: *A Hoary-headed Grebe* Podiceps poliocephalus *squats on its nest of decayed waterweeds fixed to underwater debris.*

Below: *A Great Crested Grebe* Podiceps cristatus *makes a floating nest on a raft of water plants.*

communally when it feeds. It travels in formation in slow, majestic flight, gliding and soaring at times. It nests in colonies on low islands, suddenly becoming noisy, with loud gruntings and bellowings; but may desert eggs or young if fish supplies fail.

Most of the other birds living mainly on water are waterfowl. Like other parts of the world, Australia has a number of wide-ranging species of dabbling and diving ducks. These tend to be nomadic or migratory and to be prepared to breed at any time when conditions are suitable. There are a few species which are more specialized in their requirements, and some of them are found only in Australia.

Two pygmy geese occur in northern Australia. They are small, neat ducks with short legs and small, round heads. The small but stout goose-like bills that give them their name are adapted for feeding on seeds and vegetable matter. They live on lagoons and flooded swamps. They rarely walk, resting on low or floating logs, and the nest is a down lining to a hollow in a tree in or by water.

In Australia, the White Pygmy Goose *Nettapus coromandelianus* is found only in north-east Queensland but elsewhere occurs as far afield as India. It feeds mainly on seeds stripped from aquatic plants, sedges, and grasses. The male is white, with green-glossed black on the crown of the head, back, wings, and tail, and a narrow breast band. In flight, a white stripe slants across the wing. The female is browner, with a brown line across the eye, and no breast band, but has faint brown barring on the underside. She lacks the wing bar. The male has a staccato *car, car, carwark* call; the female a soft quack.

The Green Pygmy Goose *N. pulchellus* occurs from the Kimberleys to Cape York; and in New Guinea and Sulawesi. It eats mainly the seeds of waterlilies, and it dives for food as well as feeding from the surface. The male is black, strongly glossed with green on its head, neck, back, and wings; there is a white patch across the cheek, and the white underside and tail end are finely scalloped in green. The female is

Above: *The Little Black Cormorant* Phalacrocorax sulcirostris *is an underwater fisher, often feeding in flocks.*
Below: *The Little Pied Cormorant* P. melanoleucos *is a more widespread species, often more solitary in its fishing; here it is drying its plumage after swimming.*

duller and browner; it has a brown head with white on the throat and a very slight eyebrow stripe. Both sexes have white triangles on the hind edge of the wing in flight. They have two syllable whistling calls and trills.

The Freckled Duck *Stictonetta naevosa* is a purely Australian duck with a limited distribution in the Murray-Darling basin and small areas of the south-west, although it may stray elsewhere. It requires deep, preferably permanent swamps and creeks with heavy growth of Tea Tree, Lignum, and Cumbungi. It is a dabbling duck, feeding mainly by night to filter fine plant and animal organisms out of the water. By day, it tends to rest quietly in cover. The plumage is a fairly uniform brown, finely freckled with pale buff; the breeding male has a red base to the dark bill. There is little else to distinguish it apart from a slightly peaked hind crown. In many ways, it resembles a swan rather than a duck. Nesting seems to be linked with water levels. It makes a surprisingly well-formed shallow cup nest of twigs, on branches or debris just above water level. It has soft piping notes and a fluty *whee-you* call; in display, the male has an odd, abrupt snorting call, and the female a loud quack.

The Musk Duck *Biziura lobata* is confined to Australia and is as aquatic as a grebe. It is a diving duck with short, strong legs and large feet for propulsion which are set so far back that the bird can hardly move on land. It tends to swim under water more often than on it, and hides by almost submerging. It has difficulty taking off and flies heavily with short, fast wingbeats, usually at night; it was once believed to be flightless until odd individuals crash-landed at night on shiny new roofs in isolated places, mistaking them for water. It is blackish brown in colour, barred with fine pale-brown lines and mottled pale brown on face and throat. The heavy body is carried low in the water, and the tail trails at the surface. The head is large, tapering to a stout wedge-shaped bill which it uses to crush the mussels, snails, and crayfish that form an important part of its diet. The male has a big, rounded lobe of skin hanging below the bill. It lives in permanent swamps of the east and west, and shows some dispersal at times. The nest is at the water's edge or in swamp vegetation and is usually well concealed. It is promiscuous and, although he is normally quiet, the male displays with tail raised and spread, head raised, the throat lobe inflated into a balloon and, throat and cheeks puffed out. It kicks back jets of water with a loud *k-plonk* and emits a loud combined grunt and whistle, displaying by night as well as by day. This attracts females for mating; subsequently the females nest alone.

The Black Swan *Cygnus atratus* feeds in and out of water. Black, with a red, white-banded bill and red-irised eyes, and with crimped wing feathers, it comes as a surprise to see it flying with its long neck extended and revealing flashing white primary feathers on the wings. The long neck enables it to reach down while swimming and to pull up submerged waterplants. It may even up-end to reach them. It will also graze on waterside grassland. It has a strangled, bugling call, used while swimming and in flight. It needs large, open waters and swamps with submerged vegetation. It is largely limited to southern Australia but travels long distances and can occur in very large numbers in suitable areas. The nest is a mound of plant material near or in water. The downy, grey cygnets are tended by both adults; they pull up weed for their young and may carry them on their backs while they are swimming.

Above: *The Green Pygmy Goose* Nettapus pulchellus *prefers deeper lagoons and swamps and feeds mainly on waterlily seeds.*

Below: *The Freckled Duck* Stictonetta naevosa *looks for permanent, well-overgrown swamps where it dabbles for small organisms at the surface, mainly feeding at night.*

One rail rates as an open-water bird. This is the Coot *Fulica atra*. Squat, black, and almost tailless, with strong legs and lobed toes for swimming, it has a stout, white bill and a bony white forehead shield. It is widespread throughout Australia on lakes and swamps, as well as across much of the Old World. It spends most of its time swimming, and its bulky cup nest is built on vegetation or on branches in the water. It has an abrupt *kowk* call and prolonged noisy *kek-king* in its frequent aggressive chasing and kicking fights. It dives and brings up waterweed to feed on. Pairs are often accompanied by complaining young; they are downy and black with orange heads or they may be grey feathered with white on the throat and neck. Although it needs a pattering take-off, it can make sustained high flights, often doing so at night when it is safer from predators.

Above: *The long neck of the Black Swan* Cygnus atratus *is designed to reach down below the water and haul up weeds.*

Below: *The heavily built Musk Duck* Biziura lobata *shows the broad body low in the water, and the odd, pendant lobe below the stout, food-crushing bill.*

Shallow water can be exploited by long-legged waders in various ways with their different types of bills. Largest and most conspicuous of the 'jab-and-snatch' feeders is the Jabiru Stork *Xenorhynchus asiaticus*. The only Australian stork, it also ranges as far as southern Asia and, in Australia, from the Kimberleys to Queensland, and less often to New South Wales. It stands about 1.2 metres (almost 4 feet) high, half of which is long legs. The neck is long, the bill long and stout. The underside, mantle, and wing coverts are white, the rest is black, glossed with blue-green. The bill is black, the legs red, and the iris a staring, pale yellow on the female and dark on the male. It strides through shallow water and swamps probing with its great bill; it takes small creatures, such as fish and crabs or reptiles and rodents. It will also feed on carrion. Pairs stay together, and a big stick nest is built high in a large tree and reused. It has a few rare deep calls and bill-clattering displays. It flies with neck and legs extended; with slow wingbeats and some soaring.

The heron family is another group of 'jab-and-snatch' feeders. In these, a stealthy approach is helped by a special joint in the neck that gives a kinked appearance but enables the bird suddenly to straighten it, shooting head and bill forward at high speed.

There are two common and widespread herons, the larger White-necked Heron *Ardea pacifica* standing nearly 1 metre (3¼ feet) high, and the smaller White-faced Heron. The latter also occurs north to New Guinea and Indonesia. The White-necked Heron is dark blackish grey in colour, with black legs and feet. The head and neck are white with dark spots on the foreneck; the underside is white streaked, and breeding birds may have maroon plumes on the back and wings. In flight, white patches show at the angle of its dark wings. The White-faced Heron is pale blue-grey in colour with a white face, black bill, and yellow legs. Both birds feed by stalking slowly through shallow water, swampy grassland, or waterside vegetation for small creatures of all kinds. The White-faced Heron also hunts on mudflats, coasts, and on offshore islands. Flight is slow and dignified with heavy wingflaps; the neck is folded with the head resting back on shoulders, legs extending back. The White-faced Heron is sometimes casual about folding back its neck for short flights. The calls are harsh croaks. They perch and roost in trees, and the large stick nests are built in them. The White-necked Heron usually nests in trees in or near water, and usually in a loose group; while the White-faced Heron is sometimes found well away from water and less frequently in groups of pairs.

The Nankeen Nightheron *Nycticorax caledonicus* is a squat and more heavily built heron. It is widespread in Australia and as far as Indonesia. It is light chestnut above, creamy below and on the face, with a black cap and two long, slender, white plumes hanging at the nape. The yellow-irised eye is set in bare green facial skin, the bill is black, and the legs and feet are yellow. Immature birds have brown-and-white streaked plumage. It rests communally by day hidden in shady trees, flapping out at night to hunt in shallow waters and swamps. It has loud, croaking calls. It builds a loose stick nest in trees or in bushes, usually in colonies. It sometimes nests with other colonially nesting waterbirds, and will steal eggs and young.

Spoonbills have the long-legged, long-necked build of storks, and fly with neck and legs extended, but the bill is long and broad, flattened above and below and widening out to form a spoon-shaped tip. They feed by wading, swinging the part-open bill from side to side through the water and seizing any small creatures that are touched. The Yellow-billed Spoonbill *Platelea flavipes* is limited to Australia and occurs on small inland waters – pools, farm dams, tanks, and clay-pans. Although there is some overlap, the Royal Spoonbill *P. regia* is found mainly on larger, shallow inland and coastal waters. Both birds have white plumage with the front half of the face bare of feathers. In the former species, the bill and legs are yellow and the facial skin is pale pink with a bordering black line. Breeding birds have spiky breast plumes. The latter has black legs, bill, and face; with a large, drooping tuft of white feathers at the nape. The calls are subdued grunts. In flight, the former tends to use alternate flaps and glides instead of steady flapping. Both build sticks nests in colonies, often with other waterbirds.

Right: *The stout black Coot* Fulica atra *is an open-water rail that dives for plant food or feeds at the water's edge.*

Below and far right: *The big, boldly patterned Jabiru Stork* Xenorhynchus asiaticus *strides and wades through marshland for food. A pair are greeting at the great stick nest.*

Ibises are smaller relatives of the spoonbills, with long, down-curved, tapering bills designed for probing and picking. The Australian White Ibis *Threskiornis molucca* of eastern and northern Australia and New Guinea is white with bare black head and neck, and lacy black secondaries overhanging the tail. The widespread Australian Straw-necked Ibis *Carphibis spinicollis* has a black, purple-glossed back, white underside, and spiky, straw-coloured neck feathers. The former wades in shallow water and hunts in wet grasses, but has also invaded rubbish dumps and around homesteads in its search for small creatures. The latter also feeds in drier open spaces, taking insects and especially feeding on grasshopper swarms. They have a flap-and-glide flight, often soaring on thermals, and usually moving in lines and chevrons. They nest in crowded colonies, often mixed with other waterbirds, in trees, bushes, or among low swamp vegetation. They are noisy when breeding, displaying with ruffled feathers and a babble of low-pitched calls; this is more like barking in the White Ibis and deeper grunts in the Straw-necked Ibis.

Waders of the shorebird group contribute the smaller species that feed by wading. The Red-necked Avocet mentioned in Chapter 1 uses an upcurved bill in the way that a spoonbill does. The stilts have extremely long legs. The Pied Stilt *Himantopus himantopus* is slenderly built with a long, very thin bill and pink legs which are as long again as the body and neck. It is white with black wings and back, and there is black on the nape and hind neck. It has partly webbed feet. It wades up to belly deep, but picks much of its food from the surface. It has sharp, yelping calls and flies strongly with rapid wingbeats and with long legs trailing back behind. The nest is a sketchy cup on a small island or tuft of vegetation in the water. It often breeds colonially.

The Pied Stilt is widespread in warmer parts of the world, but the Banded Stilt *Cladorhynchus leucocephalus* is peculiar to Australia and is adapted to life on the salt lakes. It occurs only on salt lakes and brackish estuaries. It resembles the Pied Stilt in shape, but it is white with black-tipped wings which are also black on the upper surfaces and have a white hind edge. Adults have a broad chestnut breast band which tapers to a black streak on mid-belly. It has webbed feet. It is a sociable bird, feeding at times in flocks of thousands, taking brine-shrimps. Birds may feed in close-packed masses and will also swim. They breed on inland salt lakes

Far left: *A wading White-necked Heron* Ardea pacifica *takes a fish with a quick bill stab; it is swallowed head first.*
Left: *The Nankeen Nightheron* Nycticorax caledonicus *roosts in cover by day and flies out to wade and fish at night.*
Above: *Commonest of the Australian herons, the White-faced Heron* Ardea novaehollandiae *rests in trees near water, and builds its bulky stick nests in them.*

after rain. They nest simultaneously, usually in huge flocks, on the bare edges of the lakes. They make a bare scrape with no nest and the eggs and downy chicks are white, camouflaged against the salt pan.

Some terns also use freshwater for feeding. These are gull-like, grey-and-white birds with black caps. The wings are long and tapering, the tail forked, and the flight is buoyant and agile. Marsh terns swoop to snatch up small creatures whereas sea terns plunge-dive to catch fish and shrimps underwater.

The Whiskered Tern *Chlidonias hybrida* is a marsh tern. In breeding plumage, its cheeks are white, the underside is dark grey, and the sharp, tapering bill red. It occurs on lakes, lagoons, inland swamps, and flooded claypits, and in some brackish waters. It has a buoyant flight, usually working low, head to wind, and dipping to snatch food from the surface; occasionally it will dive. It is a widespread, nomadic Australian species which also occurs in other parts of the Old World. The bird breeds in colonies, making nests on the low

vegetation growing in water. The call is a sharp *kitt* or *kittit*, with noisier variations at breeding colonies.

The shorter-billed Gull-billed Tern *Gelochelidon nilotica*, with shorter tail and longer legs, is also a freshwater tern of lagoons and swamps, visiting estuaries and coasts. In addition to snatching food from water, it will also hunt on dry land. It has short, rasping calls. Widespread except in the arid centre of Australia, it also has a worldwide distribution. It nests colonially on low islands or sand spits in lakes, nest construction varying according to the amount of material nearby.

The great Caspian Tern *Sterna caspia*, with its big, scarlet bill and heavy, gull-like flight, also occurs on larger inland waters and estuaries as well as at shallow coasts. It is another worldwide species; it is migratory or nomadic in Australia and is usually found in regions near the coasts. It plunge-dives, often from a height. The call is a deep, harsh *kraa*. It nests, usually singly or in small groups, on bare islands or sand spits of fresh or brackish waters.

The small plovers use open, barer water margins, feeding in typical fashion with short fast runs, ducking to pick up insects or other small animals. They bob their heads when nervous, and make rapid low flights. Australia has three native species. The Red-kneed Dotterel *Erythrogenys cinctus* occurs in muddy margins of inland swamps, lakes, and lagoons, often among dead and fallen trees. The Black-fronted Dotterel *Charadrius melanops* prefers the stony or

Above left: *The Royal Spoonbill* Platelea regia *is a bird of larger, shallower waters, feeding by swinging its flattened bill from side to side in the water and catching tiny animals.*
Below left: *The Straw-necked Ibis* Carphibis spinicollis *catches small creatures on dry land as well as in shallow water, but nests in colonies in swampy places.*

Above right: *Pied Stilts* Himantopus himantopus *have very long legs for wading that can make mating an awkward process.*
Below right: *The Banded Stilt* Cladorhynchus leucocephalus *is adapted to life on saline lakes and estuaries of Australia.*

Above: *Banded Stilts often form large flocks on saltpans where food, such as brine shrimps, may be abundant; they nest in close colonies on the bare margins of such places.*

shingly margins of creeks, rivers, and small streams. Both occur widely throughout Australia. The Hooded Dotterel *C. rubricollis* occurs on the margins of salt lakes in the south-west and on more open sandy coasts in the south-west and in the south-east.

The Red-kneed Dotterel is brown on the back, and black on the head, nape, and lower breast, surrounding the conspicuous white patch of throat and upper breast. The black of the breast extends on to the flanks to meet a chestnut patch; the belly being white. The long legs are red down to the joint, then blue-grey. The hind edge of the wing is white in flight.

The Black-fronted Dotterel is mottled brown on the back, with a purplish-chestnut shoulder patch. The crown is light brown with a white eyebrow stripe bordering it. Black extends as a streak from the centre forehead, back across the eyes to the nape, and down either side of the breast to form a broad V on the mid-breast. Otherwise, the throat and underside are white. In flight, it shows a white wing stripe and tail tip.

The Hooded Dotterel is brown above, white below, with a black head and throat, a broad white nape band extending to the hind cheeks bordered with black. In flight it shows a white wing stripe and a black, white-edged tail. In all three species, the immatures are white on the underside, with fainter indications of adult patterns on the head and back.

The Red-kneed Dotterel has a trill, and a *chet, chet* flight call; the Black-fronted Dotterel a sharp *pink* and *chip-chip-chee-chee-chee* flight call; and the Hooded Dotterel a deeper *kew, kew* and low flight calls. All have rapid, level flight but the Black-fronted Dotterel has broader, more rounded wings, and a distinct, 'flipping' wing flap.

The nests are scrapes on open ground near water, often by a plant tuft or dead branch. The downy chicks run soon after hatching.

The more heavily vegetated swamp areas attract a number of birds, including those for which open water is not the primary requirement. The biggest bird of this habitat is the Australian crane, the Brolga *Grus rubicunda*. It stands up to 1.25 metres (4 feet) high, with long legs and long neck, the long secondaries overhanging the tail. The bill is dagger-like. The plumage is ashy grey, and the bird has a bare red face and nape and blackish bulge on the throat. It lives in long-term pairs that often gather in flocks when not breeding. It feeds on plants and small creatures, taking them in open grassy areas and in swamps where it also digs for roots and corms with its head sometimes submerged. The call is a loud, trumpeting whoop that may be extended to a series of shorter, harsher notes. It is given on the ground and in flight. Pairs indulge in dancing displays, ducking, bowing, and leaping with wings spread, and sometimes throwing twigs. Displays are accompanied by trumpeting calls which are usually given with head thrown back and the closed wings lifted. The flight is slow and deliberate, with the neck and legs extended. The nest is a large heap of plant debris on the ground, often in a shallow swamp; northern birds breed in the wet season. It occurs throughout the north and east but has become greatly reduced in the south of its range.

The Magpie-goose *Anseranas semipalmatus* is also a swamp bird. It is black with white across the mantle, rump, and inner wing coverts and on the underside. It has a prominent knob on the forehead, and bare skin around the eyes and nostrils. The strong, narrow bill has a small hard hook at the tip. The legs are long, the feet half webbed, and it wades and walks well. It can also perch easily and may rest and roost in trees such as paperbarks. It has broad wings and the deep, deliberate wingbeats are more like those of a bird of prey. It strips seeds from grasses and rice, and digs for sedge tubers and spike-rush bulbs. It also swims and up-ends for food. It was once present in eastern Australia but is now limited to the north; it is also found in New Guinea. It breeds in the wet season, pulling down reeds and trampling them to form platforms on which to display and to nest. Some males

Above: *The muddy and often tree-cluttered margins of inland lakes are the feeding places of the Red-kneed Dotterel* Erythrogenys cinctus. *It also nests at more vegetated sites.* Right: *The Whiskered Tern* Chlidonias hybrida *is a marsh-feeding and marsh-nesting species, snatching food from the surface.*

have two mates. The nests may be substantial cups. Adults help the downy young by bending seed heads, by pulling up submerged plants, and by dropping billsful of seeds in front of them. This is the only waterfowl known to drop food directly into the mouths of young. They do not moult all the flight feathers at once and, unlike other waterfowl, they do not become temporarily flightless.

The harriers are wetland raptors. Harriers usually fly low, alternating flapping the long wings with gliding on wings held in a shallow V. The tail is long, the legs long and thin. A harrier relies on surprising its prey, usually the weaker birds and mammals, and dropping on them. The Swamp or Marsh Harrier *Circus aeruginosus* hunts in this fashion, and may also hover heavily. It perches on posts, on stumps, or on the ground. The nest of sticks and stems is built on the ground, hidden in tall swamp vegetation. The female incubates and tends the young, the male bringing the food. The male is dark-brown above, greyish on the wings, with darker-brown to blackish barring. The underside is buff streaked with brown, and there is a white band across the rump. The female is browner. It has weak, high-pitched, whistling calls. It occurs in the wetter swamp areas of Australia, and throughout much of the Old World.

The Spotted Harrier *Circus assimilis* is blue-grey above and rufous on its underside and face, with fine white spotting and whitish barring. The duller immatures are more like Swamp Harriers. It is a bird of drier, open places, Saltbush or canegrass swamp, but it builds a stick nest in a low tree. It is found throughout most of Australia.

Tall growth of reeds, rushes, or Cumbungi, or grass tussocks provide cover for a skulking heron, the Australian Bittern *Botaurus poicilopterus*. About as big as a White-faced Heron, but with a thicker-looking neck, it sneaks through the vegetation in a horizontal, crouching stance. Its plumage is yellow-buff, heavily mottled and blotched with blackish brown, with dark streaking on a paler underside. The bare facial skin is green or blue, and the legs are greenish. It flies reluctantly and low, with heavy slow beats of broad wings, soon dropping into cover. It hunts mainly at night taking all kinds of small creatures. It can grasp stems in its feet and walk through reeds above water level to peer over the tops. The male is polygynous and has a deep, hollow boom – a *woomph* note like that produced by blowing over the mouth of an empty bottle. The nest is a platform of plant material in swamp vegetation at water level; the female nests alone. The Bittern is limited to south-west and south-east Australia.

Many of the rails rely on wetlands. The small species are skilled skulking birds and are rarely seen. The waterhens are typically adapted to life in wetlands. The large Swamphen has already been mentioned for its adaptation to urban park waters. Another species tending to follow its example is the Dusky Moorhen *Gallinula chloropus* of the better-watered areas of eastern and south-western Australia. It is dark olive brown above and blackish below, with white outer edges to a short tail which is frequently flicked upwards. The yellow-tipped bill and small forehead shield are scarlet, and the long legs and long toes are greenish. It runs easily on land in search of its food of plants and small animals. It can perch, and it swims well with head jerking in time to the kicking feet; it feeds at the surface in deeper water, in the way that a coot or duck does. It prefers to run but can fly well.

The varied calls are sharp and explosive. It may occur in pairs or in flocks. The cup nest is built in water vegetation or in tall plants by water. The downy young are black and fluffy and swim well from the start.

The Black-tailed Native Hen *G. ventralis* is similar to the Dusky Moorhen, but has a few white flank streaks and a larger, laterally flattened black tail that can be cocked up like a domestic hen's. The legs are red, the shorter bill with smaller shield is green with a pink base to the lower mandible. It is adapted to the uncertain rains of the drier inland. Unlike the Dusky Moorhen which ranges to New Guinea and Indonesia, it is confined to Australia. It is similar in habits to the former species, but spends more time on dry

Above: *Black-fronted Dotterel* Charadrius melanops *at its nest.*
Below: *Brolgas* Grus rubicunda *dance in display.*
Overleaf left: *The Pied Goose* Anseranas semipalmatus *grubs for roots with its strong bill in northern swamps.*
Overleaf right: *Swamp Harrier* Circus aeruginosus.

land. It is gregarious and nomadic, appearing and disappearing overnight in large numbers. Where rains have made inland swamps temporarily suitable, it will appear and nest, often in large, loose colonies, with nests on the ground among bushes near water. It is fairly silent, but has a harsh, metallic, cackling call. In dry periods, it moves to more permanent swamps.

Above: *Like the Swamp Harrier, the Spotted Harrier* Circus assimilis *hunts by gliding low over swamps and low vegetation and pouncing; but nests in trees.*

Below: *The Black-tailed Native Hen* Gallinula ventralis *is a sociable, nomadic species of inland swamps, invading temporarily suitable areas and breeding after rains.*

Right: *A skulking, terrestrial cuckoo of grassy places, the Pheasant Coucal* Centropus phasianus *builds a domed nest hidden in ground vegetation, and rears its own young.*

Above: *The tiny Golden-headed Cisticola* Cisticola exilis *builds a fragile domed nest bound to plants with spiders' webs.*

The Pheasant Coucal *Centropus phasianinus* is a cuckoo of the swamps. It is large and pheasant-like, and is long tailed and short legged. It is a skulker and usually identified from its song – a deep, hollow, and slowly accelerating series of *coop* noises, like water gurgling from a bottle, and often emenating from down among long vegetation. It has a short, curved bill, red-irised eyes, and a stealthy walk and run. It snaps up any small creatures it chances upon. It flies slowly and awkwardly, and crash-lands into vegetation. The plumage, which is barred and streaked is patterned for camouflage among grass like that of a quail or buttonquail. It is rufous brown above and yellowish below, but, when breeding, it moults to black, with chestnut wings and back. It is not parasitic and makes a sketchy cup nest on the ground, concealed in vegetation pulled over to form a dome. It occurs in the north and east near coasts.

The tall swamp vegetation also attracts small insectivorous birds, with some confined to it. Most are skilled skulkers, heard but seldom seen. A possible exception is the tiny Golden-headed Cisticola *Cisticola exilis*, present in northern and eastern coastal lowlands, and also extending north to China. It is a little, short-tailed warbler, rufous buff with creamy underside; the crown and back, but not the nape, are heavily streaked with black. The breeding male's head and rump are a bright golden buff. From a conspicuous perch or in jerky flight, it sings a loud incessant buzz note followed by a click-like liquid *lek* or *pillek*. Low chatters and a nasal *chew* call are also heard. The nest is domed and built of plant material bound together and to living leaves with spiders' webs. The male is possibly polygynous and the female does the nesting duties.

10
Coasts and Islands

The birds of Australia's coasts and islands include landbirds that use the shore and island habitats, and seabirds that must come to land to breed. For landbirds the coasts offer the safety of islands for breeding, although the habitat may be more like a severed fragment of mainland. In addition, coastal habitats offer beaches of sand or shingle, mudflats and sandflats in sheltered bays and inlets, and rocky spits and cliffs. These coasts also offer a refuge to shorebirds escaping the northern hemisphere winter, and to resting seabirds.

For seabirds Australia bridges two regions. To the south, there are the rich seas where the subtropical and subantarctic zones meet. This region is rich in seabirds, such as penguins, and the albatrosses, shearwaters, and petrels. These reach southern Australia, but mostly as stray or offshore birds, with only a few species breeding, mainly in the Bass Straits and Tasmanian areas. The shores of northern Australia are those of the tropical seas, used by tropical seabirds, such as boobies, tropicbirds, and terns. True seabirds are hesitant to come to land except when necessary for nesting so that for these birds, the shore may often be a momentary resting place, while for breeding, the different-sized inshore and offshore islands are more important.

The Cape Barren Goose *Cereopsis novaehollandiae* is a landbird associated with coasts. It occupies the grassy areas of islands of southern Australia, from the Furneaux group in the east to the Recherche Archipelago in the west. A heavily built, small-headed goose, it is grey in colour with blackish spots on its wing coverts. A fleshy, pale-green cere covers the nostrils and the upper part of the bill which is short and stubby. Cape Barren Geese graze on grass and herbage. The birds pair for extended periods, and the males aggressively defend territories. The females have grunting calls and the males also have loud, harsh honks. The nest is a down-lined scrape on the ground, and the downy young are boldly striped in brown and grey. Immatures form flocks which stay together for several years. They fly freely between islands and to the nearby mainland.

A more unexpected bird of coasts, often seen flying over the sea, is the large fruit pigeon, the Torres Strait Pigeon *Ducula spilorrhoa*. It is attracted to these areas because they offer safe sites for its nesting colonies. It has a seabird-like colour pattern, in white with black flight feathers on its wings and tail. It is a summer visitor from the New Guinea area to northern coasts from the Kimberleys to north-east Queensland. It feeds on rainforest fruits, particularly figs. A

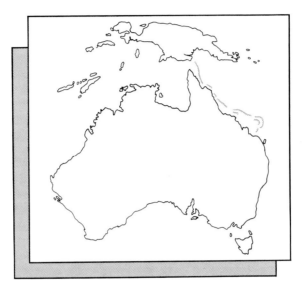

few may remain through the dry season. It normally breeds in colonies on islands with mangroves or rainforest. The birds fly out each morning to disperse through mainland forest; and return in late afternoon. A few nest in coastal mangroves in Northern Territory. Large colonies off the Queensland coast may number 20000 to 30000 birds although, in the past, colonies may have been much larger. Nests may be only a few metres apart. The colonies are noisy places; males make loud advertisement calls, low *coo-woos*, on returning to the colony. The frequently displaying males press the bills to swollen breasts and bow with very loud *coo-hoo-hoos*, and there is a sharp note of aggression. They fly swiftly on long, pointed wings. Pigeons normally share incubation, with the male sitting most of the day, but, in this species, they incubate on alternate days to allow the necessary feeding flights. Because they are so conspicuous they are suffering from disturbance at colonies, as well as from extensive felling of rainforest

Another landbird that uses coasts and island habitats, as well as inland sites, is the Banded Rail *Rallus philippensis*, about the size of a domestic pigeon. It is streaked light and dark brown with some white flecks on its crown and back, barred black and white on the underside with an orange-buff breastband, and has a chestnut band across the ashy grey face to a chestnut nape. The bill is stout and tapering. It tends to occur singly or in pairs, and sneaks through low cover in hunched posture with an upward-flicking tail. It is active mainly at dusk and at night. Near human habitation it may become tame. It is present near east and west coasts, and in the Arnhem Land region, usually in low-lying or swampy areas. It is nomadic and, from the south of its range, migrates to New Guinea. Its overall range extends north to Sulawesi and the Philippines, and through many islands. In Queensland, in particular, it occurs on offshore islands with some cover, where it may become more open in its behaviour and scavenge on the shore. It will also steal eggs and small chicks from the smaller seabirds such as terns.

There is a small grass parrot that lives on coasts. The Rock Parrot *Neophema petrophila* occurs in the south and south-west. It feeds on the seeds and fruits of salt-tolerant plants of beaches, dunes, estuarine flats, and rocky, coastal promontories and islands. It is drab olive brown in colour with a touch of blue on its face and forehead and along the edges of the wings. It usually occurs in pairs or in small parties, feeding quietly and unobtrusively. When it flies, it is swift and jerkily erratic, with intermittent glides, and it lands in a sudden flutter of wings. It usually feeds early and late in the day, resting quietly on a low perch at other times. The flight call is a plaintive *tsit-tseet*, and it has a quiet twitter when feeding. It prefers to nest on a small island or rocky promon-

Left: *Typical of many shores is this sandy beach beaten by surf but piling small vegetated dunes on the landward side, and with occasional projecting rocky headlands.*

Above: *The Cape Barren Goose* Cereopsis novaehollandiae *is restricted to the islands and nearby mainland.*
Below: *Although it is a forest-feeding fruit pigeon, the Torres Strait Pigeon* Ducula spilorrhoa *is exceptional in nesting colonially on islands and flying daily to the mainland for food.*

tory, a little above high-water level in a rock crevice, often behind creeping plants.

The sea coast, with its supply of fish and other sea creatures, provides support for some raptors. The Brahminay Kite has been mentioned in an earlier chapter as a bird of the mangroves and nearby shores, but the one most highly adapted to fishing is undoubtedly the Osprey *Pandion haliaetus*. The big bird of prey is brown on upper parts and white on head and underparts, with a brownish band of streaks across the breast, and a dark-brown stripe across the yellow-irised eye and down the neck which, with the thin head and sharply hooked bill, give it a haggard look. In flight, it is reminiscent of a large gull, the wings long and arched, with a dark mark at the angle. The legs are long, and the strong feet have long, narrow, curved claws with rough lumps at their bases to help grasp slippery fish. The bird hunts over water at heights of up to 50 metres (160 feet), spotting fish and dropping and plunge-diving with legs extended, sometimes disappearing except for raised wings, emerging with the fish in its foot, and shaking the water off its feathers as it flies away. The outer toe can twist back for a better grip, and large fishes are carried, head first, in both feet, torpedo fashion. It has high-pitched whistles and cheeping calls. The Osprey occurs sporadically around the coast, except in the extreme south-east or Tasmania. It will travel up estuaries and the lower reaches of larger rivers. It also occurs in most parts of the world. It builds big nests of sticks and debris. These are re-used and refurbished to become great piles on trees, or drum-shaped structures on ledges or on the ground on lonely shores or islands.

The other coastal raptor is the White-bellied Sea Eagle *Haliaeetus leucogaster*. Larger than the Osprey and nearly as big as the Wedge-tailed Eagle *Aquila audax*, this is Australia's other big raptor, also ranging north to India and

southern Asia. In flight, it is a large, broad-winged bird looking mainly white, and with a majestic, slow-flapping, soaring flight. The back and wings are deep grey in colour with darker primary feathers, and there is a narrow dark band on the base of the tail. The tip of the tail is tapered. Young birds are brown with white patches, visible in flight, under the primaries and a dark tail tip. It drops from a low level over water to snatch fishes, sea snakes, or waterbirds. It also kills a large variety of birds and other animals. It will rob other birds of food and will eat carrion. It does not dive. It uses perches to give it a wide view and, in addition to hunting the seashores, it will also occur on larger inland rivers and lakes. It uses nasal, goose-like, clanking calls, often given as a duet with raised bills. Like the Osprey, it builds and re-uses a huge stick nest in a tree if available, or on rocks or on the ground of promontories and islands. As with other raptors, green leafy twigs may be added while it is nesting.

The open beaches and tidal flats are used by shorebirds. Some are resident. The Bush Stone Curlew of open woodland has a counterpart in the Beach Stone Curlew *Burhinus neglectus*. This is just as large as the former but has shorter, stouter legs, a heavy body, shorter tail, and a great bill, which is long and deep and looks too large for its head and unnecessarily massive for its diet. It is uniform greyish brown on its crown and back, greyer on the tail, pale grey on the breast, and white on the belly. Blackish forewing coverts

Above: *The Banded Rail* Rallus philippensis *is a larger rail of low-lying areas that also breeds on islands where it may scavenge and predate seabird colonies.*

Above: *The Osprey* Pandion haliaetus *is a fishing raptor, swooping to seize prey from just below or at the water surface.*

Left: *The White-bellied Sea Eagle* Haliaeetus leucogaster, *here with a catfish, is a coastal and island predator and scavenger, able to snatch food from the surface of the water.*

with a narrow white hind border show as bars on the closed wing, and the secondaries form a pale ash-grey patch. White inner primaries form a big white triangle in flight, the outer ones black with a white patch near the tip, while the under-wings are mainly white. It tends to stand around a lot by day, but will catch crabs with its big bill. It rests in the shade of mangroves or shoreline trees. It flies with deliberate beats of down-curved wings, legs trailing. At evening and at night, it becomes active and noisy, feeding on various small creatures and, like the Bush Stone Curlew, calling with long-drawn eerie whistling cries that rise to a crescendo and then

Above: *The great bill of the Beach Stone Curlew* Burhinus neglectus *helps it deal with thick-shelled prey such as crabs.*
Below: *The Pied Oystercatcher* Haematopus longirostris *is a conspicuous and noisy birds of muddy and sandy shores with a stout chisel bill for opening shellfish.*

become shorter and die away. They are higher pitched and harsher than those of the former. It also has a rather feeble double alarm note. It uses exposed reefs, mangrove borders, and quiet open beaches and flats, from Shark Bay around the north to New South Wales. It is also present north to Borneo and the Philippines. The two eggs are simply laid on a bare sandscrape, often among flotsam and debris.

The Pied Oystercatcher *Haematopus longirostris* is a bird of sandy beaches and sandy and muddy tidal flats and estuaries around Australia; it is commoner around Tasmania and scarcer in the north. It is a sturdily built, largish shorebird. Strikingly patterned, it is black above with a black breast shield. The rest of the underside is white. The legs are pink, the long, strong, blunt-tipped bill is scarlet, and the iris of the eye and the bare eye rim are red. In flight it shows a black tail, white rump, and short, white stripe on the wing. It is replaced on rocky shores and stony beaches by the Sooty Oystercatcher *H. fuliginosus*, which is similar but has an all-black plumage.

It probes for marine worms and molluscs, and uses the bill to open bivalves such as cockles. It is a self-assertive bird, conspicuous and noisy in flight and on the ground. It has a penetrating, piping *kleep* call. In frequent displays a pair runs side by side with bills pointing downwards, rapidly repeating an accelerating series of *pic* calls that run into a trill. Several pairs may perform as a party. This species maintains a nesting territory in which the nest is a simple scrape. Food is brought to the downy young for a while; later they feed themselves, but they can run and swim from the first, and will crouch motionless when alarmed.

The Red-capped Dotterel *Charadrius ruficapillus* is a small beach bird. It is a plump, long-legged little plover that scuds across open sands on twinkling legs like something blown by the wind. It is white underneath and on the front of the face, and pale grey-brown on the back. The crown and nape are orange-chestnut, the forehead and face white with a narrow black line on the forecrown and another through the eye and bordering the cheek. The female is less orange-

chestnut. It is often inconspicuous against sand or shell beaches until it takes flight, to show a narrow white wing stripe and a white-edged dark tail. Flocks of non-breeding birds often show the rapid, co-ordinated flock flight which is so typical of small shorebirds. The calls are a sharp *wit* note which may run into a trill, a more musical *pu-wit*, and a *kit-tup* flight call. It is widely dispersed around coasts and islands, on low, sandy or muddy shores and dunes, but it may also occur inland on bare shores of salt lakes. Pairs defend breeding territories in which the nest is a scrape ornamented with a few stones, shells, or plant fragments.

Some of the shorebirds that regularly occur on the coasts are migrants from the northern hemisphere, evading the northern winter by sharing the Australian summer. The Large Sandplover *C. leschenaultii* occurs round much of the Australian coast, although it is found mainly in the northern half. It breeds from the Middle East to Mongolia. In Australia, it is sometimes found in company with the extremely similar but slightly smaller Mongolian Sandplover *C. mongolus* which breeds from the higher Himalayas and Tibet north to the Pamirs. Both may occur as migrants; solitarily or in flocks, sometimes of both species. They feed on beaches, sandspits, mudflats, estuaries, and on tidal mud.

Left: *This small ginger-headed shore plover, the Red-capped Dotterel* Charadrius ruficapillus, *occurs on bare sandy areas.*

Below: Shorebirds resting on a beach include Mongolian Sandplovers C. mongolus *in breeding and intermediate plumage, and* Great Knots Calidris tenuirostris *in the background.*

The Large Sandplover is about half as large again as the Red-capped Dotterel. It feeds more stolidly and, if disturbed, tends to run or fly only a short distance. It is sandy brown above and white below. The stout, black bill may be nearly as long as the head. The forehead and face are white with a dark line through the eye and on to the cheek. The Mongolian Sandplover is a little darker brown, more white behind the eye, with a shorter bill and darker face mark, but identification can be uncertain. In flight, both birds show a thin white wing stripe. When developing breeding plumage, both show rufous across the breast and on the nape, and black across the face and round the white forehead. The Large Sandplover has a clear *tweep-tweep* call and a soft trill, the other a harder, sharper double note.

The Grey-tailed Tattler *Heteroscelus brevipes* is one of the slender-bodied, sandpiper types of shorebirds with long legs, neck, and bill. Little known on its breeding grounds in north-east Siberia where it feeds in stony riverbeds, it occurs in considerable numbers on northern Australian coasts although it is less common in the south. As a wintering migrant, it prefers large areas of sandflats or mudflats, mangrove waterways, and tidally exposed coral islets. A tidal

Left: *Although a common non-breeding visitor to Australia, the Grey-tailed Tattler* Heteroscelus brevipes *is a little-known bird on its nesting ground in north-east Siberia.*

Below: *The Reef Heron* Egretta sacra, *fisher of reefs and shores, has plumage which may be blue-grey, white, or mixed.*

Above: The Knot Calidris canutus *is a sociable feeder on mudflats, spanning the globe to visit Australia from breeding grounds on the tundra of the arctic region.*
Below: *Unlike others, the Black-faced Cormorant* Phalacrocorax fuscescens *is limited to coastal regions of southern Australia.*

feeder, it rests communally at high tide, huddled on rocks or breakwaters, or perched on mangroves. Although it is not shy, it has a nervous, energetic manner, bobbing the head and teetering and wagging the rear end up and down. It has a level flight with fast, flickering wingbeats. It has few distinguishing marks. Non-breeding birds are light grey, very pale speckled grey on breast and face, and white on the underside. There is a darker line through the eye and a whitish eyebrow stripe. The grey bill has a yellowish base and the legs are green.

The long-distance traveller among shorebirds is the Knot *Calidris canutus*. It breeds on the drier, stonier areas of Arctic tundra of the northern hemisphere. Its migratory dispersal is worldwide and, as well as reaching Australia, some go as far south as Macquarie Island in the Subantarctic. It is highly sociable. The Knot is a dumpy looking bird with a shortish neck, a black bill which is rather short for a sandpiper, and the bird is about the size of a Banded Plover or thrush. It feeds on mudflats of estuaries and inlets in small flocks, all moving forwards in a fairly close group, digging stolidly at the mud with their bills, like a mob of feeding sheep. In winter, they are grey, with paler feather edgings, and whitish on underside and eyebrow stripe. They tend to fly in close flocks with rapid, co-ordinated movements, and pack together at high-tide roosting places. They have a low-pitched chatter when feeding and low *knut* calls. The flight call is a whistled *twit-wit*. Before they leave, they may begin to show the breeding plumage which is a striking chestnut red or rust colour, with upperparts speckled with black and silver. They may be found around most of Australia's coastline on suitable shores.

The Reef Heron *Egretta sacra* is an egret which lives on sea coasts of the tropical Pacific Ocean. About the size of a White-faced Heron, it is sturdily built with a long, heavyish bill and shorter, stout legs. There are three colour phases. Birds may be dark slate-blue with white throat mark and dark bill and legs, white with yellowish bill and legs, or, more rarely, mottled blue and white. Breeding birds have long fine plumes on the nape, back, and breast. It occurs around most of Australia except the extreme south-east, and is commonest in the north. It is found on beaches, rock plat-forms, and reefs, and defends a stretch of feeding territory. It takes fish, crabs, prawns, and insects, hunting actively with a stealthy, low, crouching approach. It roosts and nests near its feeding territory, usually in a tree or shrub. The nests are typical twig platforms, built in trees, on top of low shrubs, or sometimes on the ground.

The cormorants comprise another family of fish-eating birds, some of which find their food on the coasts, and, as underwater hunters, they make use of the sea but they do not venture too far from the shore or from islands. Several Australian cormorants occur on sea coasts, but only one seems wholly associated with them. This is the Black-faced Cormorant *Phalacrocorax fuscescens*. It has a peculiarly limited distribution, on the coasts of southern Australia and around Tasmania. It occurs in very large numbers in the Spencer and St Vincent Gulfs, where breeding colonies are very big. It is black on the crown and forehead down to the eyes, and on facial skin around the blue-green-irised eyes, and on the bill. The hind neck, upperparts, and thighs are black, while cheeks, fore-neck, and underside are white. Breeding birds are white spotted on the hind neck, rump, and thighs. It is larger than the two little cormorants described earlier but it is very similar to the Pied Cormorant *P. varius* which also occurs around coasts but has bright orange-yellow facial skin and is larger, as also is the Great Black Cormorant *P. carbo*. It fishes singly, or in parties, or sometimes in very large flocks when shoals of fish are pre-sent. It flies low and fast, with shallow wingbeats and the head and neck extended horizontally. It rests and roosts in company on low perches such as buoys, breakwaters, jetties, or offshore islands. It nests in colonies on rocky islands, rock stacks, or on quiet, undisturbed headlands. The nests are mounds of seaweed and various plant debris or driftwood. Although this bird is usually silent, it has low, guttural calls at nesting colonies.

Australia is rich in coastal and island terns, with nine breeding sea terns and two noddies, in addition to non-breeding winterers or visitors. Sea terns are usually white birds with grey wings and back and a black cap. They have narrow, tapering wings and forked tails. They are agile and powerful in flight; they can hover and plunge-dive to catch small sea creatures at or a little below the surface. They breed in colonies, usually preferring offshore islands – no doubt for safety. In view of the number of seabirds that do so, it would be interesting to speculate how many of these birds Australia might not have had without these islands.

The Crested Tern *Sterna bergii* is typical of some larger terns. It is slaty grey on its back, wings, and tail. It has a shaggy naped, black cap shortened by a white band across the forehead, and a slightly droopy looking, yellowish bill. It has a rasping *karrick* call. Widely distributed across the Indian Ocean and western Pacific, it breeds around Australia although it is commoner in the south. Colonies are usually on islands, on open, sandy or gravelly areas, usually with some vegetation and near the shore. Birds are equally spaced, a double 'bill stab' apart. Even when other space is available, birds crowd together. The single egg is laid in a bare scrape, the space around consolidated with droppings. Intruders and potential predators are mobbed. The flight is buoyant and easy, dives are often made from a considerable height with birds partially submerging, and numbers may gather around fish shoals. After breeding, they often scatter, resting and roosting with other terns or gulls on beaches and sandspits. As with many terns, the forecrown of non-breed-ers becomes white, giving the birds a partly bald look.

The smallest species are the similar Fairy Tern *Sterna nereis* and Little Tern *Sterna albifrons*. The former occurs only around southern and western Australia, New Zealand, and New Caledonia. It is less than half the size of the Crested Tern, and is a pale silvery grey colour on its wings and back. The legs are short and orange. The head and bill look large; the bill is orange-yellow and the black cap is separated from the bill by a white, triangular forehead patch extending

Below left and bottom left: *The Fairy Tern* Sterna nereis, *the male here bringing food for the chick, is a small tern of sandy beaches.*

Below: *Bridled Terns* Sterna anaethetus *occur in loose colonies, the nests hidden in crevices or under vegetation, and with the off-duty bird watching nearby.*

down to the forecheek. The Little Tern is more widespread
around the world. In Australia, it occurs in the north and
east from the Kimberleys to Tasmania, replacing the Fairy
Tern except in the Bass Straits, but possibly beginning to
supplant it. It is darker grey with black wing tips; the bill is
yellow with a black tip; the white forehead triangle is separated from the white cheek by a dark streak through the eye.

The birds have similar habits. They tend to act with an air
of energetic enthusiasm, moving with fast, deep, flickering
wingbeats and high-pitched *kirridic* calls, and a rasping
kree-ik. They hover frequently before diving, plunging at

Above: *The Pacific Gull* Larus pacificus *with a more massive bill
than any other species, is peculiar to Australia.*

Right: *The Great Skua* Stercorarius skua *is a scavenging and
predatory winter visitor from the antarctic.*

Below: *The noddy terns are species of warm seas. The Common
Noddy* Anous stolidus *often makes its nest of seaweed and plants
on a shrub or rocks.*

times into very shallow water but with the same dash as larger species, raising a small plume of spray, and taking shrimps as well as fish. The nest colonies are often small and usually consist of a group of scrapes on sandy beaches. A displaying male may parade around a female, neck and bill stretched high with a small fish held up, wing tips drooping, and spiky tail almost erect. It also has a fish-showing display flight. Both species disperse and possibly migrate northwards after breeding.

The Bridled Tern *S. anaethetus*, like the similar but more specialized Sooty Tern *S. fuscata*, is a more marine tern. Both feed on fish, small squid, and plankton, and they snatch much of this by dipping to the surface without diving in the way that marsh terns do. The Bridled Tern, however, will also plunge-dive and feeds more often by day; otherwise both feed mainly at night. Both are dark plumaged. The Bridled Tern is blackish brown on the upper parts, white below, and the top of the head is black with a white forehead chevron back to the eyes. The Sooty Tern is darker still with a white streak over the eye. The Bridled Tern's wings are long, the flight swift and buoyant. It will hover and swoop, often in flocks, to pick up prey. It uses a sharp, small barking call. It is widespread around the world in tropical seas and, in Australia, it occurs from the Barrier Reef region round the north and west to Cape Leeuwin, and in St Vincent Gulf. It nests on islands. The nests are not in open crowded colonies, but are hidden under small shrubs and vegetation, in crevices under rock ledges or among boulders. They are, therefore, scattered in a loose colony. With night feeding, the off-duty bird may perch on a rock or bush while its mate is sitting. They appear to migrate northwards after breeding. In contrast, the Sooty Tern breeds in large, crowded, and noisy colonies on open ground; ringing with loud *wide-a-wake* calls.

The noddies are small marine terns of tropical seas. Like the Bridled and Sooty Terns, they feed by swooping to snatch at the surface, sometimes momentarily landing, taking fish, squid, and plankton; they probably often feed at night. The plumage is dark, with a pale cap. The tail is not strongly forked, but is heavier and wedge shaped. They can live at sea, resting on the water. The flight is swift and erratic, with long glides.

The Common Noddy *Anous stolidus* occurs around the tropical seas of the world and is found on the coasts of the northern half of Australia, breeding on large and small off-shore islands. It is blackish brown in colour; the white cap of the forehead and forecrown merges into a darker colour on the hind crown, and is sharply defined over the eyes. Unlike other terns, noddies usually nest in trees or bushes. The Common Noddy builds nests of trampled seaweed and leaves, usually in shrubs, sometimes on the ground, and lays a single egg. The name refers to head-nodding displays. Its calls include a harsh *krarrk* or *kak*, hollow *kwok*, and other

Left: *The Brown Booby* Sula leucogaster *is one of the plunge-diving seabirds of the warmer oceans. Some nest on islands off northern Australia.*

Below: *A vigorous, efficient, plunge-diving fisher, the Australian Gannet* Morus serrator *nests in close-packed colonies.*

notes. After breeding, birds disperse to sea.

Although it is rich in tern species, Australia has relatively few gulls. The commonest is the small Silver Gull, already mentioned as a species found in association with human settlement. Australia has its own large gull, the massive-billed Pacific Gull *Larus pacificus* of the southern shores. This seems to be threatened by the recent invasion and spread of the Southern Black-backed Gull *L. dominicus*, however, which is widespread around southern oceans and is now colonizing the same southern Australian coasts. The Pacific Gull has a sooty black back and wings, but otherwise it is white with a black tail band. The young are the usual dark mottled brown colour changing to adult plumage over a period of four years. Adults have yellowish legs, and the yellow bill with its scarlet tip is deeper and more massive than those of other gulls. It has deep, abrupt, gruff call notes. Like most larger gulls, it scavenges, and preys on a wide range of marine and shore animals. It will drop shellfish on rocks to break them. It will also feed on inland waters, swamps, and rubbish tips. It nests in scattered, single pairs or in small, loose colonies on islands. The cup nests are made of gathered plant material. Adults are sedentary, but young birds tend to wander.

The Great Skua *Stercorarius skua* of the Antarctic is a regular winter visitor to southern Australian coasts. It is about the size of the Pacific Gull, but is dark brown with whitish wing patches showing in flight. It is heavily built and has a more hooked bill; it is an efficient predator and scavenger. The Great Skua will fight over beached carcasses with arched neck and spread and raised wings. It breeds in the subantarctic near colonies of seals, penguins, and the like, taking eggs, killing small birds and mammals, and feeding on the dead. In its winter wanderings, it takes what

it can find, but tends to stay offshore, often following ships to scavenge.

Like the skuas, there are other seabirds for which land is a necessity only when breeding. The gannets and boobies are built for plunge-diving, with streamlined, cigar-shaped bodies tapering to a strong bill and a pointed tail, long tapering wings, and big feet for underwater propulsion with all toes webbed. They see fish from above and plummet down from a height, drawing their wings back just before they hit the water and then disappearing for a short interval. They swim well and can live at sea.

The Brown Booby *Sula leucogaster*, one of three species breeding on islands off northern Australia and present in all tropical oceans, differs in being mainly dark brown instead of white. It is white on its lower breast and belly, with a band on the underwing. The legs are yellowish. The male's bill is grey and the facial skin around the eye and bill is bluish; in the female these are yellowish. The female has low, quacking calls, the male a higher-pitched hissing. They perch on trees, rocks, buoys, or floating objects, including boats. The nest is a platform of debris built on the ground or on a rock platform, each item added with solemn bowing ceremonies, neck over neck. At sea, they occur singly or in small parties, and fish more inshore than other boobies.

The Australian Gannet *Morus serrator* is a bigger bird than the booby. It is white with black flight feathers on its wings and centre tail, and a yellow-washed head. It is a more efficient plunge-diver from up to 30 metres (100 feet), often taking shoaling fish in a close flock of plummeting birds. They fly with intermittent flapping and gliding, and travel in strings, line-astern. There are small colonies around southern Victoria and Tasmania, and some larger ones around New Zealand. Nests are placed on level areas, headlands, or raised islands; the drum-shaped structures are neatly and regularly arranged a 'bill-stab' apart. Nesting birds call and quarrel with deep *urrah* calls, and paired birds rub bills and preen each other. Young birds are blackish

with white spots, only gradually acquiring adult plumage.

The tropicbirds are also plunge-divers but with shorter, stouter bodies and a heavy head with a stout, tapering bill that at times reminds one of a large kingfisher. The three species are widespread around the tropical seas of the world, and the Red-tailed Tropicbird *Phaethon rubricauda* nests on western and north-eastern Australian coasts. It is white with a touch of black on the inner wing, and a black stripe across the eye of the broad-browed head. The bill is red, the webbed feet black. The tail has two long, very narrow red streamers, as long as the bird itself. Young birds lack the streamers and are lightly barred with black. When hunting, the bird flies over the sea in steady flight, rapid fluttering wingbeats alternating with glides; it then plunges down and submerges in dives after fish. It usually occurs in ones, twos, or small groups. It can swim, but the legs are weak and well back and, on land, it shuffles forward with breast touching the ground. Among cliffs or rocky outcrops, it nests in scattered pairs in caves, crevices, or under vegetation - the nest is just a bare scrape. Males display in flight at the nest sites, hovering and backing so that the red plumes are waved conspicuously below the bird, and pairs may fly in synchronized flights. The usually single chick is fed by the adults on regur-

Below: *The gentle-looking Red-tailed Tropicbird* Phaethon rubricauda *is an aggressive plunge diver of warmer seas.*
Above: *The Short-tailed Shearwater* Puffinus tenuirostris *crosses the Pacific Ocean when not breeding in colonies in burrows on south-eastern Australian islands.*

Left: *A long-winged, long-tailed aerial expert, the male Greater Frigatebird* Fregata minor *displays by inflating its throat into a great red balloon, both on the ground and in the air.*

gitated food, and finally leaves for sea alone.

The frigatebirds, related to boobies and tropicbirds, have abandoned diving in favour of an aerial life to a point where the legs and feet have become very small, and are little use except for perching. By comparison, the wings are huge – long, narrow, and angled – and the forked tail is long, like scissor blades. They are as aerial as swifts, and they glide, hang, soar, and twist on small updrafts and thermals as well as on sea winds, rarely flapping their wings. The long, slender bill is strongly hooked, and they swoop down and snatch fish and other creatures from the sea. They also live by piracy. They harry other seabirds, forcing them to disgorge food, and they even steal any nest material that they are carrying. They will also take chicks and eggs from nests at seabird colonies. They drink in flight, skimming over the water.

The Greater Frigatebird *Fregata minor* breeds on outer islands of the Great Barrier Reef, and the Lesser Frigatebird *F. ariel* breeds along the north coast. Males are black, with white arm-pit patches in the latter species, and females have white breasts, and a whitish throat in the former. Males of

Previous page: Islands, like this coral island of the Great Barrier Reef, are important to coastal birds, offering a greater assurance of freedom from disturbance and predation when nesting.

both have bare red throats which, in display in flight, or on a perch, are inflated into great scarlet balloons. When perched, the male vibrates this bladder and rattles the bill. The nest is a twig and-debris platform; the material which has not been stolen from other birds is pulled off in flight. There is one egg. Nests are usually located near another seabird colony that can be parasitized.

Shearwaters, petrels, and albatrosses also make great use of flight for feeding at sea. Their long, narrow wings enable them to glide for long periods, conserving energy. They also swim well with webbed feet, and make shallow dives after fish, squid, and similar marine creatures. They spend most of their time at sea, only coming to land to nest, and then usually on offshore islands. Several of the medium-sized shearwaters nest on islands around Australia, and the Short-tailed Shearwater or Muttonbird *Puffinus tenuirostris* is the best known, and possibly Australia's most numerous bird. Between May and September the birds are at sea, mostly moving on a great route taking advantage of the prevailing winds that carry them to the northern end of the Pacific Ocean and back again. In spring they return in enormous numbers to their breeding islands, stretching from New South Wales to eastern South Australia. Skilful in flight, they are awkward on the ground, and avoid danger by nesting in a burrow and visiting the colony at night. Return-

Left: *Although albatrosses may visit onshore waters, the Shy Albatross* Diomedea cauta *is Australia's only breeding species.*
Above: *The delightful Little Penguin* Eudyptula minor *breeds in southern Australia, walking ashore at night to avoid predators.*

ing birds gather in swimming or circling flocks or 'rafts' near the colony. After dark, as they fly in, the birds already in burrows call repeatedly with a loud throaty *kooka-rooka-rah*, rising in tempo and pitch, guiding the returning birds. The chick, hatched from the single egg, grows as large as the parent and is very much fatter before fledging. These are the ones that have been harvested as 'muttonbirds'.

The larger albatrosses mostly breed on subantarctic islands, but the Shy or White-capped Albatross *Diomedea cauta* breeds on Albatross Island in the Bass Straits and on two islets off Tasmania. It has a wingspan of over 2 metres (6 ½ feet). It is white with a dark-grey tail, back, and upper wings; the underwings are white with a narrow black border. Below the distinct browridge, the side of the face is grey. The big bill is purplish or greenish grey with an orange-yellow tip. When not breeding, birds occur around southern coasts, often close inshore or following fishing ves-

sels. They take fish, squid, cuttlefish, crustaceans, and will also eat carrion. When breeding, it has the loud gurgling and guttural calls, and bill-clattering displays, typical of these birds. The nest is a large raised cup of earth, vegetation, and castings cemented with droppings; and occupied for a long period by the big downy young one.

Most aquatic of the Australian seabirds is the Little Penguin *Eudyptula minor*. It is the smallest of the penguins, and breeds only in southern Australia and New Zealand. It is only about 33 centimetres (13 inches) high, blue-grey with whitish underside, black bill, pinkish feet, and no obvious patterns; it looks tiny and vulnerable. Like all penguins, it is flightless and chases fish underwater, propelled by its flippers. It may also swim at the surface, low in the water with body awash.

It nests in a burrow or rock crevice or cavity, on islands; lining the nest cavity with plant material. It must walk to the nest and, like the shearwaters, comes ashore after dark and leaves before dawn. It has sharp, yapping contact calls, and a high-pitched braying during displays. Two young are reared. Birds disperse after breeding, but return to the burrows to moult; unable to fish, they are again vulnerable.

Index

Acknowledgements

The publisher would like to thank Neil Curtis for editing this book, Richard Garratt the designer, Moira Dykes the picture researcher, Curtis Garratt Limited for providing the maps, and Barbara James for the index. Special thanks to the Frank Lane Picture Agency for all their help. Tom and Pam Gardner/Frank Lane Picture Agency provided many fo the photographs except for the following:

Ardea, London pages: 33(below left),53, 57(below), 61(top), 69(top), 77(below), 85(both right), 87(top), 94, 112(top),116(top), 117(top), 121(below),122(below), 135(top), 138(below),144(below), 150, 152(top), 164(bottom right), 169. **Bruce Coleman Ltd** Jen and Des Bartlett pages: 15 (below), 56. G Bingham

pages: 171(below). Brian Coates pages: 50(top), 78. Alain Compost pages: 52. AJ Dean pages: 15(top). Frithfoto pages: 61(below), 71(top). Graham Pizzey pages: 57(top), 174(below). Hans Reinhard pages: 20-21, 21, 25(centre), 77(top), 143. Joseph Van Wormer pages: 109. **Frank Lane Picture Agency** pages: 2-3, 33(below right), 168, 175(top). Hans Dieter Brand page: 42. Christiana F. Carvalho page: 12. David Hollands pages: 11(top),30, 49(centre), 102-103, 104(top left and below), 160(below). Eric and David Hosking pages: 29(left), 40(top), 49(top), 86-87, 104(top right), 112(below), 115(below), 133(top left), 138(top), 142(top), 166(below), 180(right), 188. G.J.H. Moon pages: 10(below), 28, 29(right), 36(top), 37(left), 41, 162-163, 180(below left), 183. Fritz Polking pages: 175(centre),

184. Len Robinson pages 1, 8, 17(top),18(top), 24(top and bottom left),25(top), 26, 32, 36(below), 38(top), 39, 46, 49(below), 58(below), 65(both),67(top), 69(below), 71(below),75, 76(top), 78, 84(both), 85(top left), 88(top left), 92-93,93, 98(both), 99(below), 105(topleft and below), 107(below), 110,121(top left), 123(below), 125,129, 130(below), 131(below), 134,139(below), 140(top), 146, 167(top).Leonard Lee Rue page: 174(top).Roger Tidman page: 156(below).Roger Wilmhurst page: 29(top).Winifred Wisniewski pages: 43(below), 107(top), 111(top), 128(below), 130(top), 140(below),151(below), 167(below), 179(below),181(centre). **Dr Colin Harrison** page: 82 **NHPA** Ralph and Daphne Keller pages: 14 (below), 68(top),

89(below),156(top).A.N.T. pages: 73, 94-95, 96(below),139(top), 142(below), 153.D + M Trounson pages: 74(top). **NHPA**W. Chapman pages: 10(top), 54-55.G. A. Cumming page: 54(top).A. Eames page: 158(below).R. H. Green page: 22(top).C. Henley page: 87(below).W. Lawler page: 67(below).W. Peckover page: 58(top).J. Purnell pages: 13(top), 54(below left).E. E. Zillmann page: 54(below right). **Oxford Scientific Films**M. Austerman/Animals Animals page:66(top)Ronald Templeton page 51(top).Babs and Bert Wells pages: 23(bottom two), 29(centre), 38(below),60, 116(below), 124(both), 127,131(below), 132(top), 133(topright), 135(below), 145(top),147(both), 148, 149, 151(top),170(below).K. G. Preston-Mafham/Premaphotos Wildlife page: 44.